SHRAPNEL

ISSUE #12   THE OFFICIAL BATTLETECH MAGAZINE

SHR▲PNEL

THE OFFICIAL BATTLETECH MAGAZINE

Loren L. Coleman, Publisher
John Helfers, Executive Editor
Philip A. Lee, Managing Editor
David A. Kerber, Layout and Graphic Design

Cover art by Ken Coleman
Interior art by Jared Blando, Brent Evans, David A. Kerber, Seth Kurbound, Chris Lewis, Marco Mazzoni, Natán Meléndez, Victor Moreno, Ben Myers, Marco Pennacchietti, Klaus Scherwinski, Anthony Scroggins

Published by Pulse Publishing, under licensing by Catalyst Game Labs
5003 Main St. #110 ▪ Tacoma, WA 98407

Shrapnel: The Official BattleTech Magazine is published four times a year, in Spring, Summer, Fall, and Winter.

Available through your favorite online store (Amazon.com, BN.com, Kobo, iBooks, GooglePlay, etc.).

ISBN: 979-8-9853599-4-7

GAME FEATURES

COMMANDER'S CALL
FROM THE EDITOR'S DESK

At ease, MechWarriors! This issue marks the close of *Shrapnel*'s third year, and before we start into year four, I want to take the time to thank all of our loyal readers. We've made a lot of improvements to the magazine since our humble first issue, and we couldn't have gotten this far without you all! Plus, there's plenty more coming, so make sure you keep your 'Mech's fusion engine banked and are ready to go when the call comes.

As a way to say thank you, we have two nice surprises in this issue. First: for the first time ever, each story in this issue is accompanied by brand-new art. Now, you may be asking, "But Commander, where's the brand-new art for the final part of Tom Leveen's *Three Ways Home* serial?" Turns out you've already seen it: the fantastic cover art from Ken Coleman helps close out this chapter of Cadet Ixchel Marquez's story. Half of the new art comes courtesy of Jared Blando, who really knocked it out of the park, and the rest is from the equally stellar Natán Meléndez.

Second: Who doesn't like mercenaries? (Besides Takashi Kurita, I mean...) Soldiers of fortune are one of the fundamental building blocks of *BattleTech*, and many fans cut their teeth on tales of Wolf's Dragoons or Grayson Death Carlyle's Gray Death Legion. The next *BattleTech* Kickstarter campaign, launching on **23 March 2023**, will focus on mercenaries, and what better way to celebrate this than to pack this issue with more mercenary content than you can shake an autocannon at? Get hyped with not one, not two, but *three* mercenary-themed Unit Digests; a *MechWarrior: Destiny* Mission featuring a merc-filled movie shoot gone wrong; a look at the best ways for a fiscally responsible merc to stretch their C-bills; a glimpse at Rahway II, the mercenary R&R-resort planet; a playable Star League-era scenario pitting the Northwind Highlanders against friends and family who serve in the Star League Defense Force; and for the mercenary on the go, the Mercenary Entertainment Network Digest—the perfect way to make sure you stay current on all of your popular holovid shows while out on maneuvers.

For fiction, we have stories from four new authors. Kelvin Casing's "Without Warning" demonstrates the lengths civilians and militia will go to oppose Draconis Combine occupiers, and "Winning the Battle, Losing the War" from Jason DeSouza follows a recon MechWarrior who dreams of heroics in battle. Robert Schubert's "One Thousand" celebrates the millennial anniversary of the Second Donegal Guards, and James Kirtley takes us through the mercenary hiring halls of Galatea in "Never Trust the Recruitment Posters."

From our veteran authors, Alan Brundage's "It Ends in Fire" kicks things off by chronicling the waning days of Clan Nova Cat's war against the Draconis Combine during the Dark Age. In Charles Gideon's "The Shoulders of Giants," a direct follow-up to "Protector of the Blood" from issue #7, Wolf-in-Exile Dara instructs his last student while on the run with the Kell Hounds. "Dying Breed," by Geoff "Doc" Swift, follows the travails of a *solahma* warrior from the Scorpion Empire, and James Bixby's "Foolproof" brings us an explosive look at the development of the heavy Gauss rifle. Finally, in Craig A. Reed, Jr.'s Age of War tale "Three White Roses," a regent's bid for power seeks to exploit the young First Prince Alexander Davion.

I also want to make a special shoutout for the Kickstarter backer characters who appear in Jason Hansa's Technical Readout: JN-G9B *Jinggau*: Nova Commander James Mitchell (Jonathan Mohring), Staff Sergeant David Heth (David Heth), Lieutenant Adam Ingersoll (Adam Ingersoll), and *Sao-wei* Vivian Lee (Lauren Bevilacqua).

For those of you who've been with us since our first issue, thanks again for a great three years. And for those who've just arrived here from the recruiter, we're thrilled to have you along for the ride as well.

—Philip A. Lee, Managing Editor

WITHOUT WARNING

KELVIN CASING

SILVAN BASIN
VERTHANDI
DRACONIS COMBINE
6 JULY 3023

"No!" Abel Tapper let out the involuntary cry as the katana swung down toward Wade Larsen's neck. He was too far away to make out much detail in the fading light, but he saw the old man's head slump forward into a grotesquely unnatural position as the blade cut deep. Queasy, he looked away as the weapon swept down a second time to finish the job.

What did Wade do to deserve that? he thought. The elderly mayor wasn't a risk-taker. He'd been almost pathological about staying out of trouble with the Dracos. If the village was harboring rebels, it was certainly against either Wade's knowledge or his will.

"Move it!" shouted the loyalist militiaman behind Abel, shoving him forward with the heavy butt of a Magna laser rifle. Abel stumbled and fell to one knee, hampered as always by his stunted and withered left arm. "Up!" snarled the soldier, hauling him to his feet and pushing him forward again. "Get moving, or we'll fly you out to the great desert and you can walk back."

As Abel struggled forward, he saw Alpha, the huge moon low on the horizon, rising behind Vannas. Between the moonlight and the dancing reflections of burning buildings on the waterlogged rice paddy, he could make out soldiers swarming through the village. Loyalist "Blues" and Combine troops were going house to house. Each one saw its door kicked in, the occupants dragged outside. Whatever the reason their card got marked, Abel knew the stories. Most settlements picked out for this kind of special attention were never heard from again.

The soldiers had emerged from the jungle only minutes earlier, without warning. Abel had been finishing up in the rubber-tree plantation when a militiaman yanked him from his AgroMech. Now he was being herded through sodden rice fields toward the settlement, while soldiers massed everyone in the village square.

Abel felt a dull vibration in the ground and looked down in confusion at his own stumbling feet as if they might be the culprit. The vibration steadily grew into booming impact tremors, and moments later two BattleMechs burst through the thick jungle surrounding the village of Vannas on all sides. Both machines carried an air of deadly menace, although one towered over the other.

Years ago, back when Verthandi was still in Lyran Commonwealth hands, Abel and his older brother Evander had been obsessed with 'Mechs. They'd spent months reading everything they could find in one of the Regis libraries whenever their parents went into the capital. Abel still remembered enough to identify the larger, vaguely humanoid 'Mech as a 55-ton *Dervish*, the smaller insectoid one as a 20-ton *Locust*. Two tanks rolled in behind them, but Abel had no idea what kind they were.

A *crack* of gunfire echoed off to the right, and Abel looked over to see a militiaman stagger out of the Mitchell farmstead, clutching his stomach. Brett Mitchell was right behind him, hunting rifle to his shoulder. He fired again, catching another Combine soldier in the side and spinning him onto the ground. Brett's youngest daughter Hannah appeared at an upper window, screaming for her father to come back.

The *Dervish* stopped, turned, and leveled one of its massive forearms. It fired a brilliant green bolt that bathed the entire village in an eerie supernatural light, casting wild and monstrous shadows. Wood exploded into flame as the medium laser cut into the farmhouse—slicing through roof, upper floor, and Mitchell himself. Then the 'Mech loosed two missiles from the same arm, transforming the farmhouse into a cloud of fire and smoke that boiled skyward as fist-sized splinters rained down across the fields.

The *Dervish* resumed its thunderous advance toward the village square, flanked by the tanks, their turrets swiveling.

They'll kill us all, Abel thought hopelessly, *or turn us into slaves for the mines. Hell, it amounts to the same thing.*

He had no family left in Vannas, but plenty of friends. He thought about them meeting the same fate as Mayor Larsen—kindly old Larsen, who'd helped his parents secure an Ericksson *PickerMech* on loan so Abel could work the fields despite his arm. Old Larsen who sat on his porch in the evening, sipping akvavit and laughing that he was "just killing time till time kills me."

Larsen and everyone else in Vannas were kind about Abel's disability, but he'd always felt useless. Useless when his older brother had joined the rebels, useless on the farm, useless when the Dracos had dragged off his parents most of all. That sense of inadequacy, of uncertainty, followed him everywhere—except inside his 'Mech. There, Abel felt he could do anything; his withered arm didn't matter.

But Abel hadn't been in his 'Mech when the militiaman grabbed him. He'd been outside checking the claw when the angular nose of a laser rifle had dug into his lower back. So now what should he do? What *could* he do? Years of working the fields had left him in good shape—besides his arm, of course—but he had no weapon. *And even if I had a rifle*, he reflected, *it'd be useless against 'Mechs. I don't want to end up like Mitchell.*

Abel thought of Evander, of how his brother had joined the rebels at the first opportunity. He'd wanted to go with him more than anything, to help in the fight. "Who needs a child soldier with only one good arm?" his brother had said gently, and all Abel's protests had fallen on deaf ears. "Look, I'll have my hands full without worrying about my kid brother out there, okay?"

Maybe his brother had wanted to keep him safe. Maybe he just didn't want to be picking up his tasks in the rebel army like he had on the farm. "You won't make a difference out there, and Mom and Dad need you here," he'd said. But less than two years later Evander was dead, his shredded remains found and identified. And then the Combine had come for his family.

To protect Abel from the Dracos, his parents had pretended he'd died during childbirth. Records were patchy enough from the Lyran handover that the ruse had worked, especially as the Combine *did* find a record of his mother's close call with influenza when she was carrying him. In reality, her sickness had only left him with one useless limb. His parents would be in the southern mines now. *If they're even still alive*, he thought.

Abel's reverie was broken when the *Dervish* abruptly stopped. Its massive feet churned the watery ground into foam as it turned. Abel followed the towering 'Mech's gaze back toward the *Locust*. He'd forgotten about the smaller 'Mech, but now saw it hadn't advanced at all. For long seconds, the two war machines stood motionless, staring at one another like enormous statues, and Abel guessed they were on comms.

Then one of the tanks opened fire on a fleeing huddle of villagers. Clutching hastily gathered possessions and each other's hands, the people were cut down by laser fire just before reaching the cover of a tall jute field. Their twisted, flash-cooked corpses tumbled away into the long grass and darkness.

Abel's vision swam with the afterglow of the laser fire, but he could still feel the dull thud of the *Locust* slowly backing off. *Maybe he's not too keen on this job*, Abel wondered as the *Dervish*'s blunt arms came up again—this time leveled at the *Locust*. The smaller 'Mech froze, and Abel found himself willing the pilot to move, to get out of there.

Suddenly, twin missiles arced out of the jungle and exploded on the *Dervish*'s rear torso, just as it triggered its own weapons. Knocked off target, the *Dervish*'s missile and laser fire crashed into the ground only a few dozen feet from the *Locust*, covering it in a wave of steaming water and boiling mud. At this, the *Locust*'s pilot finally seemed to wake up, swinging their machine into a birdlike run, even as another pair of missiles flew out of the jungle and hit one of the *Dervish*'s legs.

Rebels, thought Abel with a sudden jolt of hope, but the *Dervish* merely twisted and launched a salvo of long-range missiles into the thick jungle, transforming it—and anyone hiding inside it—into a blazing inferno. Then the 'Mech turned its attention back to the *Locust*, firing a volley of short-range missiles from the ends of both arms. The smaller 'Mech dodged too late, and one warhead impacted against its right leg, scattering shards of armor. The *Locust* opened up with its medium laser, scoring a white-hot line down the *Dervish*'s thick chest, but doing little real damage.

The militiaman had stopped pushing Abel forward now, instead staring open-mouthed at the sudden internecine conflict above them. *Now or never*, Abel thought and seized his chance.

Slamming his good arm into the man's throat, he barreled into him and knocked him backward into the muddy water. Then Abel brought his right foot down hard on the man's spluttering face. He heard a sickening crunch and the militiaman's watery scream, but he was already off and running for his AgroMech.

The night sky lit up as the *Locust* fired its medium laser again— missing the *Dervish* entirely, but scoring a lucky hit on the rear of the tank immediately behind it. Abel saw the crew jumping from the flaming vehicle as it rolled to a stop, only to be cut to pieces by a barrage of machine-gun fire from the rebels advancing into the village square. Combatants on both sides dived for cover as the firefight ignited.

Moving fast and low, Abel saw the dark wall of the rubber-tree plantation looming ahead, black against the starry sky. He could just make out the running lights of his AgroMech, which still sat with one clawed hand locked around the base of a tree he'd been in the middle of moving.

Just a little farther...

A missile impacted behind him, the explosion tossing him forward into the plantation like a ragdoll. He hurtled into a tree, shattering the tapping bowl and dousing himself in the milky white latex it was extracting. Blood streamed from a cut on his forehead and ran into his eyes as he pulled himself up and dizzily staggered onward.

Relying on his good arm, Abel heaved himself up the chain ladder still unrolled on his AgroMech's side. He pulled himself through the hatchway into the cramped cabin and hastily punched the controls that brought the machine humming to life.

Abel's 'Mech was physically powerful, yes, but also slow, cumbersome, and armored only as a hedge against tumbling rocks or falling trees. It was not designed for combat. Regardless, he felt the same surge of excitement he always did when in control of this lumbering beast. A rush of adrenaline coursed through him as he fastened his safety harness and grabbed the controls, specially customized so a single stick and two pedals could command the bipedal giant. Then he urged his machine forward through the trees, angling back towards the rice fields and Vannas.

As the AgroMech plowed into the darkness, laser burns suddenly hissed and sizzled on its torso. Abel spotted the militiaman who'd grabbed him earlier, his face now a bloody ruin, firing from the trees to one side. He spun up the AgroMech's left-hand threshing attachment and swiped at the soldier with the whirling blades. In truth, he'd only meant to drive the man off, but the industrial mechanism caught the small figure's center mass, instantly transforming his body into a cloud of bloody droplets that spattered softly against the cabin's canopy.

Ahead, explosions of light and fire confirmed the *Dervish* and *Locust* were still hard at it. Abel burst through the tree cover to see the fight had not gone well for the smaller 'Mech. One of its stubby arms had already been torn off, and its legs and torso were charred black. In comparison, the few hits the *Dervish* had taken didn't seem to have slowed it at all.

The *Locust* swiftly circled the *Dervish* in a wide arc now, occasionally pelting the heavier 'Mech with bursts of machine-gun fire from its remaining arm. For its part, the *Dervish* seemed unbothered as it tracked the *Locust* with its lasers.

We need to work together to have any chance of taking that thing down, Abel thought and grabbed his earpiece to open the comms, but a voice was already crackling to life there.

"*Locust* to...to whatever the hell you're in," said a woman's tense voice. "You hear me? Over."

"I hear you," said Abel trying to sound calm. "I hear you, *Locust*."

"Call me Razor. You armed?"

Abel looked out at the small laser precariously mounted on his 'Mech's left arm, added to deal with the most troublesome roots and branches. "Just a laser."

Razor was silent for a moment. "That'll have to do. Go for the rear while I keep him busy. He's already taken some hits there. Make it count."

The *Locust* charged the *Dervish*, machine gun blazing, then swung away, trying to retread its previous course. The nimble 'Mech had managed to dodge several shots from the *Dervish*'s lasers already, but now one beam caught its knee dead-on. Abel, relieved to be shielded from the brilliant light behind his polarized viewport, saw the laser burn through the lightly armored joint and slice into myomer muscles.

The *Locust* staggered and slowed, dragging its now useless limb behind it. The *Dervish* closed in for the kill, back still turned to Abel's AgroMech. Either the pilot hadn't noticed him or didn't consider him a threat.

Time to change that, he thought, as he drew closer.

The AgroMech's small laser was only effective over a short distance, but at point-blank range from the *Dervish*'s back, it could still do some serious damage. Abel lined up the arm and fired. Armor bubbled and hissed under the crimson beam, leaving a ragged cut down the *Dervish*'s back. Abel's cold sweat turned hot as the temperature inside the cabin spiked.

The *Dervish* turned, confused as it seemed to assess the newcomer. Somehow, the looming monster was even more terrifying now than when Abel had been on foot. There, he'd been running and dodging, with barely time to glance at the war machines battling overhead. Now he was staring directly into the *Dervish*'s menacing torso, its glistening missile ports.

One good hit and I'm scrap metal, he thought.

Then the *Locust* triggered its weapons, laser beam and machine-gun rounds crashing into the *Dervish*'s back, deepening the wounds there. The larger machine turned again, and this time fired without hesitation, short-range missiles pummeling the *Locust*'s remaining leg. *He's trying to take her alive*, Abel thought, wondering what punishment the Dracos would have in mind for a MechWarrior turned traitor.

"Hit him again!" shouted Razor, her words barely audible through the hiss of static.

Abel moved his 'Mech at an oblique angle to the *Dervish* and lined up his laser on its rear torso once more. They were making progress. Armor plating now hung off the *Dervish*'s back, and bundles of loose wires sparked and sizzled in the night air.

The *Locust* fired with its medium laser to keep the larger 'Mech's attention, but the *Dervish* had already anticipated Abel's move. Before he could fire a second time, the *Dervish* twisted back toward him and unleashed its own right-hand laser. The shot was perfectly placed, smashing into the AgroMech's flank and slicing through the jury-rigged laser as well as part of the cabin. Molten metal droplets spattered against Abel's calf, and he screamed as they burrowed into soft flesh. Then the *Dervish* swung back to the *Locust*, which was still staggering forward, machine gun blazing.

Nauseous from the pain in his leg, gagging from the acrid smoke filling the cabin, Abel barely resisted the urge to vomit. His vision edged with black and drifted like he was underwater. He saw disjointed images: the control board screaming for attention, his hand moving in staccato jolts under the strobing flash of warning lights, the dog-eared safety manual on his console.

Abel stared out at the melted left arm of his 'Mech, now a grotesque parody of his own body. The *Dervish* hadn't even bothered to finish him off. The enemy pilot assumed he was done for—an inconvenience to be dealt with later. True enough, Abel had no other weapons. And once the *Locust* was toast, so was he.

And so is Vannas, he thought.

A missile exploded against the *Locust*'s torso, rocking the 'Mech backward, and the *Dervish* quickly followed up with a laser beam that carved off its remaining arm and silenced the hammering machine gun.

"Get out of here," panted Razor's voice in Abel's ear, "This thing's almost over."

As Abel's head cleared, he looked at the *Dervish*'s ruined back. *Dammit, one more good hit might do it*. He glanced at his AgroMech's right arm, wishing they'd mounted a laser on that side as well. Abel realized he hadn't even released the arm's heavy utility claw in his rush to the fight, which was still clamped around the tree he'd been replanting. *It looks like a club in the hands of some mythical giant*, he thought distractedly. Then he almost laughed aloud.

The *Dervish* was standing over the *Locust*, readying its killing blow when the twelve-meter tree slammed into it, knocking it sideways and onto one knee. The pilot had no time to recover as Abel brought up the thick trunk again, this time smashing skyward into the *Dervish*'s cockpit.

"Take that you bastard!" he crowed as the impact sent the 'Mech sprawling backward into the muddy water. He raised the makeshift club to strike the *Dervish*'s head again, but the tree exploded into fire and cinders as the prone 'Mech unleashed its lasers.

Weaponless once more, Abel tried to bring his AgroMech's foot down on the *Dervish*'s torso, but his machine was too clumsy, too slow. The *Dervish* rolled sideways in one elegant move, then fired again.

Short-range missiles devastated what little armor the AgroMech still had on its left side. Shrapnel ripped through the cabin, slicing into the control couch and slashing at Abel's back. As he slumped forward in pain, the AgroMech stumbled and fell, smashing into the watery ground with a deafening roar that sent a small tsunami washing over the fields.

Both machines now lay next to each other, the *Dervish* on its back, Abel's AgroMech on its side. But while the *Dervish* was down, all its weapons were still intact. Abel's own 'Mech had nothing left. Given half an hour, he might be able to right the machine—but he was down to seconds.

Yet those few moments slowed to a crawl as the *Dervish* brought up its arm and Abel stared straight into the twin missile tubes nested there. Bruised, bloody, and beaten—there was nothing he could do and nowhere he could go. He was helpless.

Abel was close enough to see the enemy pilot through his ferroglass canopy, but it was impossible to know if his opponent was smiling triumphantly behind that bulky neurohelmet. Nor could Abel see any look of horror as a shadow loomed over the *Dervish*'s head and one of the *Locust*'s birdlike feet smashed down into the cockpit, crushing man and machine in a shrieking cacophony of twisting metal.

Silence rushed in like air into a vacuum. For what felt like hours, Abel lay very still in his control couch, unable to move or even to think. Slowly, he fumbled with his harness, unlocked it, stood, and clambered toward the cabin hatchway. He left a trail of bloody handprints on the viewport as he steadied himself inside the wildly tilted and ominously creaking space.

After kicking open the hatch, he emerged into warm night air clogged with greasy smoke. For a moment, everything was quiet but the hiss and ping of cooling metal. Then Abel heard a distant cheer go up from Vannas. Amid the burning buildings, waving rebels stood atop one of the Combine tanks.

Weak and nauseous, Abel half climbed, half fell from the AgroMech's head and splashed into the rice paddy below. The warm, muddy water felt gloriously cold on his sweat-covered body. He staggered toward the *Locust*, but no hatch opened.

Abel jumped as a voice burst the stillness. He'd forgotten he was still wearing his earpiece.

"That was some piloting," said Razor, coughing. "Taking him with only one arm."

For a moment, Abel thought she must be able to see him, but then realized she meant his AgroMech. "Thanks," he replied. "You coming out?"

He heard her rasping laugh. "I think I'll just stay here for a while," came the quiet response.

Abel looked at the *Locust*'s cockpit high above him. Deep gouges had been torn through the canopy. Slowly, the *Locust* pulled its leg free from the *Dervish*'s head in a protesting squeal of metal on metal. As it staggered backward and stopped, Abel looked at the insignia on its shin.

"You're militia?"

"On my first real assignment," she said. "Got a crash course in 'Mech piloting and they sent me out here." Her voice sounded far off now. "I...I didn't know what they were planning... I thought they just wanted to give me a live combat trial."

Abel looked at the smoking crater that had been the head of the *Dervish* and nodded. "I'd say you passed."

"Yeah...you too. We got that son of a bitch... We got him."

Suddenly, Abel found himself bathed in light as a pair of hovercraft roared toward him. He raised a hand to shield his eyes from the harsh glare of headlights. Fans whirred and whined as the vehicles twisted to a halt. Rebels jumped from the first craft and headed for the *Locust* while a man sporting a black beret and red beard stepped down from the second and approached Abel.

"Damn, feller, that was one hell of a show," said the man, putting his hand on Abel's shoulder. "We weren't expecting 'Mechs. I was about to order everyone to pull out while that monster was still busy with you two. I can't believe you brought it down...and in a damn AgroMech no less!"

"Vannas..." Abel started to say, but the man put up a hand.

"Yeah, don't worry, we're getting 'em together. They'll wanna come with us. And you too... We need guys like you."

Abel was about to reply when the hovercraft's radio blared to life. "Colonel Brasednewic, we've reached the *Locust* pilot. She's dead, bled out from a gut wound, looks like."

"Dammit," said Brasednewic, his brow furrowing. "You know 'er?" he added, looking at Abel, who shook his head. "Well, shame. We need all the pilots we can get, even militia turncoats. Still, I wonder how many of our guys she killed before her little change o' heart?"

Another rebel ran over. "Sir, that *Locust* is trashed," she said. "We can strip it for parts, but the *Dervish* looks recoverable if we can haul it to Fox Island."

"Now that'd be a real prize... Have to move fast, though." Brasednewic ground his teeth and looked at Abel. "Think your machine can help us get it out o' here?"

Abel shrugged. "Maybe... If I can get her back on her feet."

"Good enough. We need all the armor we can muster to even the score with these bastards." Brasednewic grabbed a radio handset from the hovercraft's front compartment. "All right people, two hours and we're moving out. The Dracos'll be back come daylight. Get the civvies ready to move, and send Whit and Yolev up here to help rig a 'Mech for haulin'"

Replacing the radio, Brasednewic gestured for Abel to follow him. "Let's get those wounds looked at, kid."

Dawn was just staining the horizon as the ragged column crawled out of Vannas two hours later, heading west along the old logging road. Survivors were piled into trucks, hovercraft, and even private vehicles. Rebel soldiers walked alongside them, watching the jungle warily as it grew ever more impenetrable.

In the rear, Abel dragged the defeated *Dervish*—now securely tethered to the back of his AgroMech and cutting deep furrows in the dark soil as it was pulled along. *Yesterday I was working in the fields,* he thought. *Today I'm what...a rebel pilot? How can so much change so fast?*

As he followed the column disappearing into the jungle, Abel took one last look at the smoking ruin of Vannas behind him and at the colorful, chirping chirimsims already picking at the corpses on the ground.

One thing he *was* certain about: the Dracos were going to pay.

VOICES OF THE SPHERE:
MERCENARY DEPENDENTS

WUNJI LAU

Though common wisdom states a warrior-for-hire should remain free of burdensome attachments, the reality is that many mercenaries have families they care deeply about and take dutiful responsibility for, be they spouses, offspring, or relatives. While some units are rich enough to have landholds, or even entire planets for their families and loved ones, most mercenary outfits must make difficult choices, and some noncombat roles cannot escape being in the line of fire. We asked dependent members of various mercenary units about their experiences at the fringes of war for profit.

Yirina Ogilvie, Bucklands (Lyran Commonwealth): Those few of us who are permitted to travel with our spouses but aren't tech or engineering personnel usually get placed in an out-of-the-way "safe" zone when we're groundside. If something bad happens, there's usually some escrow set aside to get the families off-world. I've only been excluded from a job one time. Series of raids on those crazy Falcons. Selby said it was even odds of them coming back, but that if they did, we'd have enough money to pay off all our loans. Oh well, at least they're still in one piece. Maybe the next job will pay better.

Hezz Odaniya, BattleCorps Legion, Albaracht (Calderon Protectorate): Once a mercenary unit gets to a decent size, it often becomes worthwhile to hire a permanent medic. Larger units even have full medical staffs and mobile facilities. We're civilians and noncombatants, but we end up in the line of fire plenty. Sometimes it's just stray shots, but some people intentionally target support units. Also, we're often the most valuable hostages or kidnap targets, so I don't go anywhere alone. So why take the job? Short answer: money. The going rate for medical staff, including performance and hazard bonuses, is vastly more than what we'd make except on the wealthiest of industrialized worlds. Sure, some of us are looking for freedom, thrills, or escape as much as the combat personnel, but there are plenty of ways for a skilled medic to live free that don't involve a significant chance of ending up as paste on a 'Mech's footplate.

Longaday Weyams, Carmichael (Federated Suns): Busybodies like to say, "This is no life for a child," but when we hit the hiring halls, I see a lot of other kids running around with their merc parents. Some folks just can't bear to leave their kids behind on long garrisons, and either bring us along (if they can afford it) or have us follow on commercial transports. It's not like there are strict rules about how kids are handled, but from what I've seen, most units do a decent job of seeing to schooling and upbringing. We're surrounded by plenty of people with training in tech, engineering, and business, so I've got a leg up on apprenticeships or academy slots. On the downside, everything I own fits in a duffel and my dating options are malfed; every guy here is twenty years older than me and runs in terror the moment my mom storms into view.

Deng Beaumarchand, Herotitus (Fronc Reaches): When a soldier leaves their nation's military for merc work, there's a pretty good chance they're dragging their family into a life they didn't expect or want. In my experience, if you couldn't hack it in House service, you won't be handling finances so well on your own. The slums of hiring-hall worlds are filled with broken families left with nothing when a merc breadwinner gets killed, Dispossessed, or vanishes to escape debts that are all too easy for an unwary merc to rack up.

Evie Shanan, McFadden's Sky Storm, Palmyra (Draconis Combine): We were with the Storm for nearly thirty years. The other spouses, significants, and relatives are all family to me, maybe more so than my actual genetic kin. We huddled around the monitors back at base during every sortie, cross-trained our duties, celebrated every successful dustoff together, held hands for every jump, wept together when we lost someone. I'm grateful my brother survived to retirement, but as much as we've earned the rest, I just can't imagine settling down anywhere without these people near me.

Mardon Kindenfellh, Panpour (Federated Suns): I haven't seen my wife in two years. She's off somewhere rimward, guarding miners or something. Part of her pay drops into our account every couple of months. Sometimes there's a bonus. The kids and I are glad when it's small; a big unannounced payout means she's dead, or good as. Death notices don't always get to families as fast as they used to. We write to each other, but delivery's irregular for that too, so there's just a lot of long silences. There's an understanding that she's lonely and I'm lonely, so we don't talk about whoever we're with when she's off on the job. Just part of the life. Knew what I was in for when I married her.

Glenn Cortez, Hansen's Roughriders: The Roughriders have a reputation for unruliness and seat-of-the-pants impulsiveness, but a lot of that is just marketing. You don't get to be one of the Sphere's name-brand merc regiments without strict financial and administrative control. Sure, fiddling with business management software and contract clauses isn't glamorous, but without me and my team, this whole enterprise rots from the inside out. The commander may have the last word on what the regiment does, but not before we've carefully gone over forecasts and line items.

To do my job properly, I need to see how money's being spent and what we're getting in return, so I travel close behind the unit and set up shop on the ground. I get the same armed escort and hazard bonuses the medics do, but if things go bad, I'm usually evacuated first, along with the records and lockboxes. I've only had to pick up a gun a few times in my career, when someone's come after the payroll, or in one case, when some particularly nasty pirates attacked the troops' kids who intern with me. After that one, the commander gave me a new doorplate: "Glenn Cortez, Combat Accountant."

IT ENDS IN FIRE

ALAN BRUNDAGE

CLAN COMMAND COMPLEX
NEW BARCELLA
IRECE
PESHT MILITARY DISTRICT
DRACONIS COMBINE
25 DECEMBER 3142

Wind whipped through Star Captain Horghuz's thick, dark hair as he sped his open-topped civilian hoverjeep across the city, and he could see it literally buzzed with activity.

After the vengeful horde of the Combine had broadcast their intent to stamp out rebellion, vast droves of the Nova Cats' lower castes were abandoning the city, taking to the nearby hills and plains. It would work out well, leaving fewer noncombatants for Horghuz and his warriors to concern themselves with once the battle commenced. Of non-Clansmen, only the true heirs of Kurita they fought for remained. All others had perished or fled, knowing their rebellion, the costly war to place a ruler beneficial to the Nova Cats on the Combine throne, was doomed.

Passing the grand cathedrals of the Bloodchapels, Horghuz's eyes instinctively sought out the chapel of Bloodhouse Winters, his bloodline. Though he was not yet Bloodnamed, might never be Bloodnamed now, still he felt a thrill at the sight of the edifice. He stepped around a crowd of technicians and laborers discussing the approach of the Combine armada, and entered the headquarters building.

Knowing the passages he needed to take, he breezed by harried guards and unarmored Elemental infantry, and headed deeper into the complex, until he arrived in a sparsely appointed office set aside for his meeting. The Star Colonel was not yet there, so Horghuz availed himself of the opportunity to sit and rest, closing his eyes for a few moments. He entered a fugue, his thoughts drifting, reliving several recent battles and the Nova Cats' utter failure to achieve their goal. He lost all track of time.

With a hiss, the door slid open, and a second hulking figure entered, taller and older than he, grizzled and bearing the weight of command. Horghuz shot immediately to his feet and stiffened to attention. "Apologies, Khan West. I was expecting to meet with Star Colonel Cox Devalis. We were to discuss my place in his battle plans."

Niko West, saKhan of the Nova Cats, stood proud and tall. Large even for an Elemental, he dwarfed Horghuz. He stared at the Star Captain from deeply recessed eyes, his gaze intent yet weary. "The Star Colonel has other matters concerning him right now. The Combine invasion force already burns for the planet. Given the precariousness of our survival in the face of this coming storm, I will make this brief. I need you to build a heavy defense Trinary that will be ready to face the Combine wherever they may land. You can do this in the time remaining, *quiaff*?"

To his credit, Horghuz gave the matter serious, if brief, thought. "*Aff*, I can do this. What manner of warriors will I be given?"

A bitter smile twisted the saKhan's lips. "You will have access to anything we can spare that still moves. Everything we can scrape together. Trainees, *solahma*, a few MechWarriors, paramilitary police, mostly infantry and tanks, even test-downs from the lower castes, for numbers if nothing else."

Frowning, Horghuz mulled that over. "The times are desperate enough. I will accept them. They shall be ready for battle no matter what. Have you any specific tasks for us?"

"None. You will be my troubleshooters, my mobile reserves. Position your forces as you will. Harry the Draconians, and prevent them from desecrating our territory. I need you to plug any holes that may open in our lines and take advantage of any opportunity that arises."

"As you command, my Khan," Horghuz said with a respectful bow.

The saKhan clapped Horghuz on the shoulder. "I knew by your codex I could count on you. The building blocks of your Trinary are mustering at Sigma Barracks. You have my permission to draw whatever you need from our stores, provided it is there. Good luck to you, Star Captain."

The saKhan spun smartly around and marched out of the office, leaving Horghuz alone with his burgeoning plans.

The barracks complex had not been used in many years, a relic from the days before the Jihad, when the Nova Cats' *touman* had been many times its current depleted size. Horghuz had set some of the volunteers to cleaning it up, and they had done an admirable job thus far.

Now the motley collection of warriors and quasi-warriors stood before him. There were many gray-hairs well past their prime, but their willingness to defend the Clan spoke volumes of their loyalty and dedication in the face of annihilation by the forces of the Combine. The enthusiasm of the newly minted warriors and former lower-caste members was infectious, giving the older warriors a much-needed burst of energy.

His new Trinary, though a Supernova in composition, was a mix of MechWarriors, tankers, battle-armored Elementals, and standard infantry. Fortunately, and despite their varied skill levels, all were prepared to do their part in the Clan's defense. Trucks rumbled up, delivering the necessary arms and equipment. Stores that had been untouched since before the Blackout were opened. Horghuz had claimed an ancient suit of Elemental armor. Its systems were well used, worn if he was being honest, but still robust. It left his less complex modern suit available to his less experienced compatriots.

Pacing the length of warriors before him, Horghuz reflected on the circular nature of life. He had been subject to such inspections in the past, now he was the one doing the inspecting, weighing the heart and soul of the warriors with whom he had been entrusted.

"Warriors! Many among the lower castes mark today as a day of gifts, and that is certainly the case for us. We have been given the gift of a glorious battle, the likes of which few of us have ever seen. Some of us have been given the gift of warrior status. I have been given the gift of you, for I shall lead you into battle and to victory!

"I know there have been doomsayers prowling the fringes of our camps, like specters in the night. They say our Clan will soon be at an end. I say they are wrong! I say we will be victorious! And in victory, there is life!"

"Seyla!" his warriors cried. It was a ragged chorus and not as enthusiastic as Horghuz had hoped, but it showed they had the spirit to face the coming days.

He turned and faced a dark, thin, nervous-looking man, who until today had been a vehicle-repair technician. "Warrior Azzad, your aptitudes show a streak of unorthodoxy. I am making you Point Commander in charge of our short-range-missile teams."

"T-thank you, Star Captain," the man stammered, his tone and posture conveying his surprise.

"MechWarrior Pardis, I have studied your codex. You tested as a Star Commander, but there was no slot available until now. I promote you, and name you my second-in-command. Should I fall, you shall lead. You will pilot one of the *Arbalest*s, and will command Support Star."

Pardis bowed her head. She had shaved her hair into a crest atop her head so she could better display the mystical tattoos adorning the sides of her skull. "As you will, Star Captain." Her voice was quiet, thoughtful, and had the faintest hint of a lisp. "May your visions guide us in all things."

A snort of derision erupted from the ranks. "Visions? Bah! *This* is where the visions of the past of led us! To the very brink of destruction!"

Turning, Horghuz faced the contemptuous speaker. It was Pwyll, a mediocre MechWarrior who had only just tested out of the *sibko*. Had the Clan not been staring utter destruction in the face and the tests not been eased for the crisis, Horghuz knew Pwyll would have been relegated to a lower caste, or perhaps perished in a Circle of Equals due to his attitude.

"This is not the time for such sentiments, MechWarrior Pwyll. We have not yet been destroyed. Save your anger for the warriors of the Draconis Combine. It is my understanding they will be here soon enough. My job is to whip you into shape. *Your* job, as the Spheroids would say, is to kill Snakes." That brought much positive murmuring from the others, though Pwyll continued to grimace.

Horghuz gestured at the piles of equipment forming. "My warriors, the tools of our trade lie here, waiting for us. Let us begin putting them to proper use."

LUCIAN FLATS
IRECE
PESHT MILITARY DISTRICT
DRACONIS COMBINE
29 DECEMBER 3142

Checking his weapons yet again, Horghuz reflected on the obvious superiority of the Elemental suit over his customary set of Clan Medium Battle Armor. It was a clear reflection of the consequences wrought upon the Nova Cats by their visions and the decisions that had followed. However, now was not the time for such musings, for the vengeful Combine had arrived.

Aerospace fighters streaked overhead, their heavy fire strafing the positions taken by the withered remains of the Nova Cat forces, optimistically designated as Alpha Galaxy. Some paltry return fire lanced upward, but they were under strict orders to conserve ammunition.

His own Trinary remained concealed, ready to spring their trap. Horghuz was impressed by how quickly his ad hoc unit, designated Provisional Supernova Trinary Rho, had come together. Truly there was nothing like a crisis to promote unity. Given more time, he knew they could be made into front-line material, but he suspected they would never have that opportunity.

Zooming in with his sensors, Horghuz watched the Combine DropShips settle to the ground with a sense of impending doom. Their ovoid hulls blocked out the sky, their thrusters kicking up great plumes of dust and debris. Against all logic and sense, their landing had been uncontested. All remaining Nova Cat aerospace assets had been assigned to a high-priority mission under the direction of Mystic Kisho, leaving none to oppose the landing. As an unblooded warrior, much to his chagrin, Horghuz had not been privy to that planning. Watching the BattleMechs march unchallenged down the ramps from their DropShips, he could only hope the mysterious mission was worth it.

The radio crackled and Pardis' voice whispered across the airwaves. "The black wave of our doom approaches. Let us set forth to meet it."

Horghuz started at Pardis' sudden speech. He was confused until he spotted the very prominent tsunami insignia on the approaching forces. The Genyosha. The Combine had sent their very best to exterminate them.

"Harasser Star, advance and target their forward elements."

"As ordered, Star Captain!"

His head-up display showed the Star's nine Cizin hovertanks darting forward at top speed. Desperately clinging to their hulls were dozens of SRM-equipped infantry, newly minted warriors with little armor and less experience. Brave or foolish, they were willing to pay the ultimate price for their Clan.

Once the tanks had almost reached the enemy, Horghuz chinned his comm. "Deploy surprise and scatter!"

The Cizins slowed enough to allow the infantry to leap off before darting away in separate directions and seeking advantageous positions. Inferno-laden SRMs struck several Combine 'Mechs. A newer model *Panther* and an older *Jenner* were wreathed in flame, blinding against the gloaming of the dusty plateau. The *Panther* was forced into shutdown, its heat sinks overwhelmed, while the *Jenner* pilot, in true samurai fashion, charged forward, a streaking figure of chaotically dancing flame intent on inflicting death and destruction. Two of the Cizins rocketed in, medium lasers spitting death. Only one took any damage before the *Jenner*'s ammunition cooked off. The pilot failed to eject, dying in their machine.

A *Phoenix Hawk L* leaped into the fray, its heavy machine guns raking the exposed horde of infantry. Scores fell, their lightly armored bodies riddled by bullets, the death of each one a punch in Horghuz's gut, but the survivors rallied and managed to inflict some damage on their killer before dying beneath a second volley. Several missiles launched at the last moment impacted the *Phoenix Hawk's* left shoulder, rendering the arm a uselessly dangling weight.

Almost time. "Support Star, hit them now!"

The quartet of Sekhmets fired first, eight large pulse lasers burning into the rest of the Combine's advance company. Seconds later, the three *Arbalest*s fired their long-range missiles in unison, raining sixty LRMs down on the Combine warriors, exploiting the damage already inflicted by the lasers. Another lance of Combine 'Mechs collapsed into heaps of ruined scrap on the ground. Confusion reigned in what remained of the enemy ranks. The timing was perfect.

Horghuz gave his next order with satisfaction. "Hammer Star, finish them."

The Jousts and Shodens of Hammer Star launched a full spread from their advanced-tactical-missile launchers, the Jousts following up with their large lasers. The remaining lance and a half of Combine 'Mechs reacted with admirable skill. Rather than fall back, they turned head on, weathering the fire, and advanced. Another three 'Mechs fell, their shattered limbs no longer able to support them.

The surviving trio comprised an *Avalanche* and two *Rokurokubi*s. Lasers, autocannon shells, and SRMs burst forth from the Genyosha warriors. Two of Harasser Star's Cizin were immediately destroyed, while the remainder of the infantry, including Point Commander Azzad, burst into red clouds under the autocannon barrage, their pitifully thin armor unable to withstand 'Mech-scale weaponry. Horghuz ground his teeth in frustration at the deaths of good warriors, but knew there was nothing to be done about it.

"Armor Star, forward!" The truncated Star of twenty-one battle-armor troopers bounded forward on their jets, a mixture of Clan Medium suits, Thunderbirds, his own Elemental armor, and even a pair of Gnomes taken as *isorla* from the Ghost Bears. In their desperation, everything was being thrown into the battle. "Point Three, with me. We will take the *Avalanche*."

The half-dozen armor suits converged on their target, a 'Mech they knew intimately thanks to the number of them in the *touman*. It offended Horghuz to see such an iconic 'Mech in Combine hands, though that meant he and his Elementals knew exactly where to strike to disable it.

Upon landing atop the offending 'Mech, Horghuz and his fellows ripped into it with their battle claws. An uncommon rage filled him, lending him the strength to rip away great chunks of armor. The unlucky MechWarrior tried to shake them off, but to no avail. Within moments, the members of Point Three had torn into the back of the *Avalanche*, bathing the 'Mech's delicate interior with fire from their flamers.

The wounded 'Mech listed drunkenly, but remained upright and functional, a testament to the skill of the Genyosha pilot. On another day, Horghuz would have been tempted to take them as bondsman, but not today. With the very survival of his Clan at stake, he could not afford that luxury. Filled with an unquenchable rage, he used the enhanced strength of his battle armor to punch his claw through the ferroglass. When the glass finally shattered, he saturated the MechWarrior with a burst from his underslung machine gun. Without its human control, the 'Mech collapsed, and Horghuz and the rest of Point Three leaped safely away before it fell.

Surveying the field, he saw the two *Rokurokubi*s had wisely retreated, though it denied his bloodlust a target. It was a small matter. He would surely face them again.

The comm crackled with a sudden urgency. "This is Star Commander Bal! Biccon Bridge is being overwhelmed! Any available forces, please respond!"

Horghuz checked his map and saw his Trinary was within range to assist. "Trinary Rho can be at your position in five minutes. Can you hold?"

"By the blood of the founders, we shall!" Bal sounded overcome with relief.

Horghuz switched back to his Trinary's frequency. "Rho, regroup and make for Biccon Bridge with haste!"

The flare of explosions and laser fire served as the perfect beacon to guide Horghuz's Trinary to the bridge. The remains of a *solahma* vehicle Star were valiantly holding the line, with several of the vehicles either burning hulks or immobilized, yet remained capable enough to continue fighting. Nearby, an infantry Point fired a mix of SRMs and portable PPCs at the oncoming enemy. The defenders clung desperately to their position, unwilling to surrender a single meter to the invaders.

An assault company was pushing them hard, led by a *Sunder* OmniMech. The venerable machine, one of the first Inner Sphere OmniMechs, anchored the Combine advance, marking it as a potential command unit. The Combine troops' rank and file were unimportant, but a commander made for a perfect target to demoralize the enemy.

"Rho, take the *Sunder*!"

Long-range fire burst forth from Support and Hammer Stars. Under the covering umbrella of fire, the Armor and Harasser Stars raced forward.

Explosions blossomed across the legs and torso of the *Sunder*, rocking the massive 'Mech back, but failing to take it down. It took a step forward and pulsed lasers across the Nova Cat lines. This one clearly had no intent of honoring duels.

The two forces closed ranks, each side gradually feeding more and more troops into the fight. With a sinking feeling, Horghuz watched the arrival of a mixed *Panther* lance, the light 'Mechs cutting into the *solahma* vehicles with a mixture of PPCs and plasma rifles. An older, battered SM1 erupted in a ball of fire, and he heard Star Commander Bal's death scream over the comm. The battered vehicles stood little chance, and Horghuz lamented their demise.

He spotted a thrust by a squad of Raiden armor. His forces were swamped, with no one but him available, so he ground his teeth and leaped forward to cut off their maneuver.

The lighter battlesuits had excellent mobility and well-trained pilots, possibly Draconis Elite Strike Team, but they proved no match for the superiority of his Elemental suit. With a snarl of fury, he skillfully wielded his small laser and battle claw, bounding gracefully among the Combine warriors. He channeled his rage, and before long there was nothing left of the Raiden squad but smoking remains. Yet Horghuz's desire for violence was not quenched. He leaped back into the fray in search of further targets.

A reprieve arrived when a battered pair of Nova Cat 'Mechs, a *Shadow Cat* and *Wendigo* piloted by MechWarriors Aurora and Sauvel, joined the fray. Their added firepower rocked the Combine lines back on their heels. Horghuz temporarily attached them to Support Star, swelling his depleted numbers. The surviving *solahma* infantry he joined to Harasser Star. With other units continuing to trickle in piecemeal on both sides, the battle of Biccon Bridge was rapidly becoming a decisive engagement.

A skeletal *Arbalest* raced past. Checking his display, Horghuz was only slightly surprised to see the unit's ID. "MechWarrior Pwyll," he said, "return to formation!"

"*Neg*, Star Captain! I will slay their leader and turn the tide!"

Such a foolish glory hound! Pwyll's embrace of death would be admirable if it did not get others killed. Horghuz felt his tendons creak as he balled his fists in frustration. "Support Star, render aid to Pwyll! Aurora, do what you can."

"*Aff*, Star Captain!" the *Shadow Cat*'s pilot acknowledged.

The Nova Cat forces moved fast, but not fast enough to save their companion. Pwyll had targeted the *Sunder*, an uneven match even if his *Arbalest* had been in pristine condition. In its barely operational condition, the 'Mech lasted but one exchange of fire. The *Sunder*'s close-range weaponry chewed into the *Arbalest*'s chest cavity, setting off a catastrophic engine explosion. The 'Mech vanished in a ball of golden flame, and Pwyll with it.

Horghuz closed his eyes, appalled by such a pointless death.

Still recovering their equilibrium after Pwyll's unsuccessful charge, Rho was caught off guard when a new unit appeared on the field, a short Star flashing IFF codes for the Rossei Keshik. In a daring move, a glossy, all-black Thunderbird battlesuit jumped atop a burning, overturned artillery piece, and pointed at the Combine line.

Horghuz rejoiced, for he knew that distinctive suit by reputation: SaKhan Niko West had joined the battle.

Seeing the saKhan, he felt a fresh surge of determination. West's presence also galvanized the hodgepodge of Nova Cat forces. They surged past their shattered lines, tearing into their Combine opponents like rabid beasts. Perhaps surprised by the Nova Cats' ferocity, the Combine troops rapidly fell back, and clear divide opened between the two sides.

Feeling uneasy, Horghuz slowed his own advance, using eyes and scanners, even as the saKhan and his guards raced heedlessly ahead. The Combine 'Mechs suddenly stopped their retreat and hunkered down, stabilizing themselves as if waiting for...

"Incoming!"

Combine artillery ripped into the bridge and those on it. The resulting explosions threw ferrocrete and shards of 'Mechs and combat vehicles skyward. A deep, groaning screech filled the air as the bridge tore apart, collapsing under its own weight and taking half of the mangled Nova Cat force with it.

Looking out at the smoking ruin, Horghuz's spirits sank, and he reluctantly opened his comms. "Nova Cats, retreat. The bridge is lost."

CEM PASSOS
NEW BARCELLA
IRECE
PESHT MILITARY DISTRICT
DRACONIS COMBINE
30 DECEMBER 3142

Despite facing serious losses upon landing, the Combine forces nevertheless pressed forward, inflicting their own retaliatory strikes.

By day's end, the meager Nova Cat forces had been thrown back and isolated at the very heart of the Clan's territory. The walled fortress of Cem Passos, constructed during the bleak days of the cultural reservations, was one of their last bastions.

Horghuz, caked in the grime of a seemingly endless battle, slurped a ration pack of unappealing gruel as he surveyed his depleted command. Less than half his warriors had survived yesterday's brutal fighting, a reality that seemed to apply throughout the *touman*. So many had not lived to see today, including saKhan West, who had fallen while halting a determined push by the First Sword of Light to capitalize on the Genyosha's demoralizing victory at Biccon Bridge. The survivors struggled to honor their sacrifice.

A resigned lethargy was settling over those who still lived. Most sensed the end was nigh. Horghuz felt it himself, clawing at him, sapping his resolve, but he refused to give in to despair. He was not so sure about his troops.

Pardis, as filth encrusted as he, lay on her back beside him, her presence pleasantly soothing to his raw nerves. She spoke, her voice pitched low for his ears alone. "I have seen the end, Horghuz. For us, it will all end in fire. But though we go to our deaths, we need not perish weakened by fear, if only you motivate us."

Looking up from his food, crouching on his haunches in front of a small fire, he took Pardis' words to heart and spoke to his remaining warriors. "I know many of you feel the end is coming. I feel it as much as you. The Draconis Combine seeks our complete and total destruction. And they may yet achieve it. But I am a warrior, a warrior of Clan Nova Cat. I will not give in to fear or despair. I will don my armor and face my enemy in battle. Should my armor be destroyed, I will fight them with a rifle. When my weapon is depleted, I shall face them with a knife. When my knife breaks, I shall fight them with my teeth. The enemy may kill me, but they will never defeat me. I am a Nova Cat, and I will *never* surrender!"

Though he had begun quietly, by the end he was shouting to the sky, quivering with repressed energy, his voice an indignant roar against fate. His own warriors and others close by took note and cheered.

Horghuz threw his meal to the ground, the food paste oozing into the soil. "I am done resting. Our enemies await our death. Let us go and give them death instead."

There would be no ambushes today, only straight battle. Horghuz's display was overwhelmed with Combine icons. So much the better.

"Forward, Rho!" he commanded.

He and his surviving Elementals leaped atop the remaining Cizins and charged the Combine bulwark. His few remaining long-range assets pummeled the enemy lines with the last of their ammunition.

Adrenaline surged through him as he and his truncated Point pounced on a *Jenner*, the light 'Mech a favorite of both the Combine and his Clan. He knew its weaknesses well, as did his Pointmates. While the others worked to disable the 'Mech, Horghuz gave in to his rage and tore his way through the cockpit hatch. He grasped desperately with his manipulator claw, hoping to tear the Combine pilot apart, but the MechWarrior remained stubbornly out of reach. Horghuz finally had enough and cut the pilot down with a burst of his machine gun. The *Jenner* fell, and the Point bounded free, leaving a mangled ruin behind them.

A pair of assault lances crested the rubble line, a tattered Combine mon fluttering in the breeze. Horghuz recognized the battered *Sunder* that had led yesterday's attack on the bridge. He marked it as a priority target for the Trinary, then put it from his mind.

A swarm of battle armor emerged from the protective shadow of the Combine 'Mechs, Kishi and Oni suits surged toward him, weapons blazing. He launched his SRMs at an Oni, finishing it off with a quick shot from his laser. His single reload of missiles cycled into place with a *thunk*. He promptly let it fly at another Draconian battle suit, then jettisoned the launcher. There was no point in keeping it, as they had no more missiles left in their stores. The last battle was truly upon them.

The lines blurred, creating a confounding mix. Localized jamming cut him off from his Trinary, but he waved down one Point of Elementals and gestured for them to follow him toward the *Sunder*. They bounded forward with him, moving with a terrifying unison. There was no subtlety, no tactics, only a desire to kill. They swarmed up the assault 'Mech's legs, drawing fire from its nearby compatriots. Horghuz felt his heart squeezed as he lost half his warriors to precision shots, but the rest continued to climb, heedless of death. Claws, lasers, and crude clubs inflicted slight amounts of damage on the 'Mech's armor. He roared in frustration, trying to burn through the hatch and into the cockpit.

He was just starting to make progress when his battle computer warned him of a target lock. He instinctively kicked in his jump jets and dodged most of the laser, but even that glancing shot evaporated half his armor.

He spun and landed hard, his feet clawing for purchase on the soft ground, knowing how lucky he was to have survived. He slid to a halt and faced his attacker, staring into the grinning death's-head of an *Akuma*. The MechWarrior saluted him awkwardly with one multi-barreled arm while twisting their torso to get a better shot.

Horghuz took a steadying breath and launched himself into the air. He fired his laser in defiance, knowing it would almost certainly cause negligible damage, but he was unwilling to go down without a fight. The laser hit true, succeeding in only scoring the paint.

The *Akuma*'s return fire was far more devastating. Autocannon shells whizzed by, chewing up the ground beside and below, spattering him with mud. The PPC ripped into him mid-jump, and for a moment all was lost to searing, blinding pain, followed by blessed unconsciousness.

CEM PASSOS
NEW BARCELLA
IRECE
PESHT MILITARY DISTRICT
DRACONIS COMBINE
31 DECEMBER 3142

Horghuz jerked awake, inhaling sharply. The intense focus and surprising lack of pain told him the suit, damaged though it was, had pumped him full of numbing drugs. He quickly scanned his status, causing his stomach to sink. What was left of his stomach, really. Half his left arm, his left leg, and the left side of his torso were all gone, seared away by the PPC blast. The only things holding him together were luck and a thick layer of HarJel sealant.

His remaining sensors could find no sign of his Trinary, but they showed a concentration of Nova Cat 'Mechs north of his position. Determined to die with his kin, Horghuz pushed and pulled himself forward with his remaining limbs. Warnings flashed from the suit, but he silenced them, not needing the onboard computer to tell him he was dying. Even Clan medicine could only repair so much.

Crawling across the battlefield showed him the ruins of his Clan. The evidence was clear, it had been a truly epic battle, one worthy of *The Remembrance*...except there would be no new verses in his Clan's *Remembrance*. Their culture, their history, would be lost, becoming nothing more than a footnote in the history of the Clans. If they were fortunate, the Nova Cats story would become a cautionary tale of the perils of being the junior partner in the alliance of a Clan and an Inner Sphere power.

Time passed strangely in his drugged state. His flagging strength gave out an hour or a minute later, it was hard to tell. His breath came in ragged gasps, a bloody froth crusting his mouth and spattering the screen in his helmet, and he knew his time was running out. But he had pulled himself far enough to see a small group of Nova Cat 'Mechs centered on a *Vision Quest*. Judging by its markings, it was Khan Jacali Nostra's 'Mech. And while the Khan lived, the Clan lived.

With a sudden *pop*, the jamming ceased. Voices babbled in his ears, the words making no sense to his unfocused mind until one voice cut through them all.

"Warriors of Clan Nova Cat, I, *Tai-sa* Diablo Reid of the First Genyosha, have a message for you from Yori Kurita, the glorious Coordinator of the Draconis Combine. She bids me tell you that this was your last chance, that all your lives have been expended. Too many times have you abandoned your duty to the Combine. Too many times have we faced the consequences of your actions. No more. Today, your Clan, like the Smoke Jaguars and so many others before you, dies. There will be no surrender taken, no absolution offered. This is the end of you."

The jamming resumed, brooking no response from the tiny collection of warriors. The Khan's *Vision Quest* shook its arm at the sky. Horghuz propped himself up on the stump of his left arm and faced the clouds. His eyes roamed the heavens, zeroing in on a rapidly approaching dot. It looked to be a single aerofighter approaching at high speed. A second reading separated from the first.

A missile.

It struck true, directly in the center of the Khan's formation. Radiation detectors soared as the Khan and her attendants vanished in a superheated mushroom cloud.

They have employed nuclear weapons against us, the thought flitted across Horghuz's mind.

The shockwave rushed to engulf him as well.

Pardis had the right of it. It ends in fire.

JN-G9B JINGGAU

Mass: 65 tons
Chassis: Chariot Type II Endo Steel
Power Plant: VOX 325 XL
Cruising Speed: 54 kph, 64 with Triple-Strength Myomer
Maximum Speed: 86 kph, 97 with Triple-Strength Myomer
Jump Jets: Hellespont Leapers
  Jump Capacity: 150 meters
Armor: Valiant DefCo
Armament:
  1 Type DDS "Kingston" Extended-Range Particle
    Projection Cannon
  1 Ceres Arms Model X Medium X-Pulse Laser
  4 Diverse Optics Sunfire Extended-Range Medium Lasers
Manufacturer: Shengli Arms
  Primary Factory: Victoria
Communications System: Dian-bao Comms, Heavily Insulated
Targeting and Tracking System: Dynatec Special T&T

In production for about half a century, the ruggedly effective *Jinggau* was on its way to becoming a mainstay of the Capellan Confederation Armed Forces. Mobile and well-armed, it was, as Chancellor Sun-Tzu Liao pronounced, a BattleMech for seeking out your opponent and doing them harm. However, when Victoria was invaded by the Federated Suns in 3103, the Fifth Capellan Defense Force destroyed the Shengli Arms facility to deny it to their hated enemy. The Federated Suns then sold the facility to Kallon Industries, which refurbished the plant to produce Suns designs. When Shengli's engineers first presented the Federated Suns *Jinggau* chassis after the CCAF recaptured Victoria in 3145, the updated 'Mech originally carried the *Jinggau II* nomenclature. However, this designation was quickly quashed by Capellan officials who preferred to show the plant's return to Capellan-focused BattleMechs as a return to normalcy.

Capabilities

Replacing the Gauss rifle for a Clan extended-range PPC—sold exclusively to the Confederation by Clan Sea Fox—was a deliberate choice to alleviate the *Jinggau*'s ammunition dependency while maintaining damage output and eliminating the risk of internal explosions. The armor was increased to align it with other modern CCAF cavalry designs such as the *Mortis* and *Vandal*, and the medium pulse laser was upgraded to an X-Pulse model. However, the most significant changes were buried deep within: triple-strength myomer lets the 'Mech increase its mobility when it runs hot, and a supercharger provides additional speed boosts so it can quickly close with the enemy. Finally, four tons of internal-component armoring increases its survivability and keeps the *Jinggau* in the fight longer than many of its contemporaries.

Battle History

In 3150, a handful of brand-new *Jinggau* -G9Bs were delivered to the Fourth McCarron's Armored Cavalry in time to participate in Operation Clarity, the invasion of Northwind. Their capabilities surprised the Twelfth Hastati Sentinels: while visually similar to their forebearers, their ability to accelerate after an alpha strike shocked the Republic Armed Forces defenders. During their attack on Fort Barret, the first updated-*Jinggau* versus *Jinggau*-refit duel occurred, with newly commissioned *Sao-wei* Vivian Lee in her -G9B squaring off against an RAF -G8Ar. The fight ended in a draw: the elite RAF MechWarrior eventually crippled Lee's *Jinggau* with their battery of Clan weaponry before limping off the battlefield; however, Lee survived the encounter thanks to the armored bathtub sheathing her *Jinggau*'s cockpit.

Once the Capellans departed Northwind, Countess Tara Campbell returned to Terra to assist Exarch Devlin Stone in repulsing the combined assaults from Clans Jade Falcon and Wolf. Among her forces was a salvaged *Jinggau* -G9B, now painted in the gray-and-tartan of the Grey Watch. Fighting alongside Cadha Jaffray in Scotland against the Second Wolf Assault Cluster, the rugged *Jinggau* shrugged off debilitating hits to its hips and gyro while taking down a pair of Wolf BattleMechs and pursuing a third. Smoking and battered, the *Jinggau* was still standing when Tara Campbell ordered her Highlanders to stand down.

Variants

Because the *Jinggau*'s cramped interior makes customization difficult, three standard refits based on extant models emerged over the decades. The first two were devised by Clan Hell's Horses: with *Jinggau*s salvaged after their 3078 battle with the Tau Ceti Rangers on Hsien, the Eleventh Mechanized Cavalry Cluster created the -G8Ar, which exchanges the armor, heat sinks, ECM suite, and weapons with ClanTech versions; and the -G7Lr, which retains the plasma rifles but swaps the armor, heat sinks, and lasers for Clan models. These refits proved so popular with Trinary Alpha they often swapped other salvaged CCAF 'Mechs with Allied units for additional *Jinggau*s whenever possible. The third refit, the -G9CCr, was created by the RAF in the wake of the Capellan invasion, and it replaces the -G9CC's snub-nose PPC with a Clan ER PPC.

All three variants were soon common in Federated Suns, Free Worlds League, and Republic space, the three nations refitting nearly all their salvaged *Jinggau*s to the mixed-tech specifications.

Notable 'Mechs and MechWarriors

Nova Commander James Mitchell: A MechWarrior in Trinary Alpha, Clan Hell's Horses Eleventh Mechanized Cavalry Cluster, Mitchell was the first Clan MechWarrior to receive a *Jinggau* -G8Ar to replace his destroyed *Ebon Jaguar*. He used it to great effect throughout the campaign to liberate the Word of Blake Protectorate, but he was one of the few Hell's Horses warriors who didn't join the Twelfth Atrean Dragoons before the final assault on Terra in 3078. Instead, his *Jinggau* went with him when he followed Star Captain Mycroft and the Cluster's remnants back to the Hell's Horses Occupation Zone.

Staff Sergeant David Heth: Originally an *Argus* pilot from Novaya Zemlya in the Federated Suns, Heth sadly lost his first and second wives to Capellan guns in 3138 and 3145, respectively. When a *Jinggau* -G7Lr became available, he immediately requested to swap for it, with the intention of killing as many Capellans as possible. Known for wiping out entire infantry companies, he takes a particular delight in setting field-artillery units alight to watch them explode. His wholesale slaughter of troopers has led the CCAF to place a price on his head; between that and the rumors of an extended cease-fire between the Federated Suns and the Capellan Confederation, he is thinking of going freelance to continue his private war.

Lieutenant Adam Ingersoll: A native Terran, Lieutenant Ingersoll was born and raised in Chicago, and following the motto on his family crest—*Non sibi sed patriae*, meaning "Not for his self but for his country"—Adam followed his father and grandparents into the RAF. During the Battle of Terra in 3151, Ingersoll piloted *Green River*, a *Jinggau* -9CCr command 'Mech in the Fifteenth Hastati. Shot out of his *Jinggau* at the Battle of Scottsburg, he hid as the Jade Falcons hunted down and executed any RAF survivors. Unable to link up with friendly forces before the surrender, he returned to Chicago and now spends his days in a LoaderMech, hoping for another chance to pilot a 'Mech in combat.

***Sao-wei* Vivian Lee:** Bright, telegenic, and a capable actress, Vivian Lee was a young war orphan on Shipka discovered by talent scouts looking for a fresh face. Starring as the precocious daughter in a highly rated comedy—her catchphrase "You're an idiot" repeated ad nauseam by giggling schoolkids—she parlayed her fame into a CCAF academy slot. Graduating at the top of her class, she was presented one of the first *Jinggau*-G9Bs to roll off the line. She enthusiastically throws herself into her responsibilities, eager to leave her childhood performances behind.

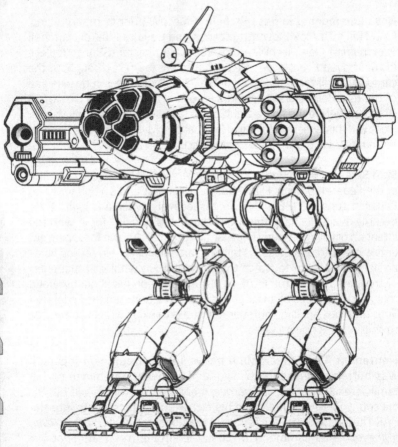

Type: **JN-G9B Jinggau**
Technology Base: Mixed
Tonnage: 65
Role: Brawler
Battle Value: 2,747

Equipment		Mass
Internal Structure:	Endo Steel	3.5
Engine:	325 XL	12
Walking MP:	5 [6]	
Running MP:	8 [9/10/12]	
Jumping MP:	5	
Heat Sinks:	17 [34]	7
Gyro (Armored):		6
Cockpit (Armored):		4
Armor Factor:	208	13

	Internal Structure	Armor Value
Head	3	9
Center Torso	21	31
Center Torso (rear)		10
R/L Torso	15	24
R/L Torso (rear)		6
R/L Arm	10	20
R/L Leg	15	29

Weapons and Ammo	Location	Critical	Tonnage
1 Medium X-Pulse Lasers	RA	1	2
ER PPC (C)	RA	2	6
4 ER Medium Laser	LA	4	4
Supercharger	CT	1	1.5
Triple Strength Myomer	LT	6	0
2 Jump Jets	RL	2	2
Jump Jet	CT	1	1
2 Jump Jets	LL	2	2
Armored Hips	RL/LL	0	1

**Download the free
record sheets for these 'Mechs at:**
bg.battletech.com/shrapnel/

Type: **JN-G8Ar Jinggau**
Technology Base: Mixed
Tonnage: 65
Role: Skirmisher
Battle Value: 2,730

Equipment		Mass
Internal Structure:	Endo Steel	3.5
Engine:	325 XL	12
Walking MP:	5	
Running MP:	8	
Jumping MP:	5	
Heat Sinks (Clan):	15 [30]	5
Gyro:		4
Cockpit:		3
Armor Factor (Clan FF):	211	11

	Internal Structure	Armor Value
Head	3	9
Center Torso	21	32
Center Torso (rear)		10
R/L Torso	15	24
R/L Torso (rear)		6
R/L Arm	10	20
R/L Leg	15	30

Weapons and Ammo	Location	Critical	Tonnage
Medium Pulse Laser (C)	RA	1	2
Gauss Rifle (C)	RA	6	12
Ammo (Gauss) 16	RT	2	2
ER Small Laser (C)	H	1	.5
4 ER Medium Lasers (C)	LA	4	4
ECM Suite (C)	CT	1	1
2 Jump Jets	RL	2	2
Jump Jet	CT	1	1
2 Jump Jets	LL	2	2

Type: **JN-G7Lr Jinggau**
Technology Base: Mixed
Tonnage: 65
Role: Skirmisher
Battle Value: 2,703

Equipment		Mass
Internal Structure:	Endo Steel	3.5
Engine:	325 XL	12
Walking MP:	5	
Running MP:	8	
Jumping MP:	5	
Heat Sinks (Clan):	15 [30]	5
Gyro:		4
Cockpit:		3
Armor Factor (Clan FF):	211	11

	Internal Structure	Armor Value
Head	3	9
Center Torso	21	32
Center Torso (rear)		10
R/L Torso	15	24
R/L Torso (rear)		6
R/L Arm	10	20
R/L Leg	15	30

Weapons and Ammo	Location	Critical	Tonnage
2 Plasma Rifles	RA	4	12
Ammo (Plasma) 10	RA	1	1
Ammo (Plasma) 20	RT	2	2
ER Small Laser (C)	H	1	.5
6 ER Medium Lasers (C)	LA	6	6
2 Jump Jets	RL	2	2
Jump Jet	CT	1	1
2 Jump Jets	LL	2	2

**Download the free
record sheets for these 'Mechs at:**
bg.battletech.com/shrapnel/

Type: **JN-G9CCr Jinggau**
Technology Base: Mixed
Tonnage: 65
Role: Skirmisher
Battle Value: 2,058

Equipment		Mass
Internal Structure:	Endo Steel	3.5
Engine:	325 XL	12
Walking MP:	5	
Running MP:	8 [10]	
Jumping MP:	0	
Heat Sinks:	13 [26]	3
Gyro (Extra Light):		2
Cockpit:		3
Armor Factor (Stealth):	211	11.5

	Internal Structure	Armor Value
Head	3	9
Center Torso	21	28
Center Torso (rear)		9
R/L Torso	15	24
R/L Torso (rear)		6
R/L Arm	10	17
R/L Leg	15	22

Weapons and Ammo	Location	Critical	Tonnage
Large VSP Laser	RA	4	9
ER PPC (C)	RA	2	6
3 Small VSP Lasers	LA	3	6
Beagle Active Probe	RT	2	1.5
Guardian ECM Suite	RT	2	1.5
Command Console	H	1	3
MASC	LT	3	3

Download the free record sheets for these 'Mechs at:
bg.battletech.com/shrapnel/

THE SHOULDERS OF GIANTS

CHARLES GIDEON

UNIDENTIFIED MINING COMPLEX
ALBION
BUENA PROVINCE
LYRAN COMMONWEALTH
5 JANUARY 3148

Dara's eyes snapped open when the scream began, and he was wide awake and rolling out of his cot before the shrill cry ended. His hand instinctively found the steel pipe he had been using as a walking stick and levered against it to hoist himself to his feet. Not sparing the time to don clothing, he hastily limped down the metal corridor connecting his environmental compartment to the rest of the complex. Dara wore only lightweight running shorts; the red fabric stood in contrast to his dark skin and the pale scars across his legs.

Sixteen months before, he had fled Arc-Royal as it fell to the Jade Falcons. He escaped on the *Dog Leg*, a DropShip owned by the Kell Hounds mercenary unit, along with hundreds of their dependents, to Albion. An inhospitable world that required living in a sealed habitat, such as the mining complex that had become their home.

As his Elemental-size strides chewed up distance with the rhythmic *clang* of his walking stick, he came to the first intersection. Several meters down the next hall, he saw a circle of children in their teens. Nearly warrior age, had they been born of Clan heritage. Their faces carried the full spectrum of emotions. Many were red with anger, some white with fear, and one boy held his arm tightly across his chest as he failed to fight back the tears in his eyes.

At the center of the circle, facing away from Dara, stood a girl. Her features were hidden under a tousled mop of hair, but he instantly knew who she was. She stood with her hands open at the sides of her head, elbows slightly angled in. Favoring her weight slightly to her back foot, she half crouched in a fighting stance Dara knew well, because he had taught it to her.

"Lowella!" he barked, his deep voice booming through the enclosed structures.

The other children immediately turned to the old Elemental and began shuffling, consciously or not, away from the space between him and Lowella. Without a word, Lowella rose from her stance, and her head and shoulders drooped.

Dara went to the boy who was cradling an injured arm, and quickly checked it with practiced hands. "It does not appear to be broken or dislocated. You are fortunate," he said dryly. "Return to your quarters and place a cold compress on it. You will be sore for several days, but you will heal."

He pivoted toward Lowella and looked her over with hard eyes. "Follow," he growled before starting back toward his quarters. Without looking up at him, she dutifully became his shadow.

As they were about to turn out of the hallway, the injured boy suddenly developed bravado. "That pup of yours is rabid!" he shouted. "She nearly took my arm off, and now you're just gonna walk off with her?! Typical Clanners. You don't belong here!" Dara had intended to let the boy's insults occupy the empty air and die there, but then he spat, "We put down sick dogs around here!"

Dara stopped midstride and planted his walking stick on the metal floor with enough force to feel the vibrations through his burn-scarred soles. The sudden noise seemed to freeze time, as only silence followed. He slowly turned his head toward the group. Anger flashed in his dark eyes as he locked them onto the slanderous little *surat*.

"I am taking her where she might learn that actions have consequences," Dara said in a low voice, dripping with menace. "I would be happy to provide the teaching a second time if I found another pupil in need of such a lesson. Shall I return for you when she has completed her session?"

The words sapped the energy from the group, and they wilted under Dara's stare. His courage faltering, the angry teen retreated into the crowd as they scrambled away.

After a few moments, Dara let out a long sigh, rubbing his weary face with a scarred and battered hand. He inhaled slowly, pushing against his steel bar as he headed toward his room. The two walked in silence, with Lowella's footfalls barely audible as she trailed behind him.

When they reached the door, he pointed to a spot in the center of the floor, and Lowella slowly walked to it, ready for her inevitable reprimand. Dara punched the button that slid the heavy door closed, then crossed the room. He spun the only chair to face his student and slowly lowered into it. Her eyes remained focused on the floor as she failed to hide her frustration and guilt.

"Explain yourself," he commanded with a sharper edge than he had intended.

"He deserved what he got," Lowella mumbled to her feet.

"I did not ask what he deserved, Lowella," Dara chided. "You will explain yourself. Or I will presume you provoked the fight."

"H-he," she stammered, trying to restrain her anger. "He said the Exiles on Arc-Royal deserved to die because they're failures, and those who died were weak fools, and any who survived were cowards!" She looked up to meet Dara's gaze, her face flushed, and her voice trembled. "So, I challenged him to a Circle of Equals, and he accepted."

"Then you attempted to break his arm, *quiaff*?" Dara asked. A quick nod was her only response. "You know these civilians do not understand our customs, even after a century of sharing Arc-Royal."

He leaned back in his chair and absentmindedly stroked the beard he had affected since their long journey from home while considered Lowella for a few long moments. She had grown taller since leaving Arc-Royal, likely due to a developmental period coupled with the planet's low gravity. Her black hair had become long and even more unruly, but her eyes retained their sharp inquisitiveness.

A twinge of remorse hit him as he thought back on their time together and realized how much stricter he had become. Being in hiding meant she was missing her *sibko* MechWarrior training, a disadvantage Dara was determined to help her overcome. They were on their third repetition of the 'Mech-piloting information he had been able to scrounge, but it was a pitiful replacement for firsthand training. *She may be the last of her Bloodline, perhaps even the last of the Clan.* Dara willed the dark thought away. *I will prepare her. I must.*

With a slight nod, he stood and began pushing the sparse furniture against the walls. "You will do your regular calisthenics routine twice," he said as he slid a crate across the floor. "One cycle for a warm-up, and one for using a contraction. Remember that you are Clan, and furthermore a Wolf-in-Exile. Our Clan gave up its place among the others to protect these people, not attack them. The sacrifices of all those who came before you require you to keep this duty. 'And the ilKhan gave us his final words,'" Dara said, starting a verse from *The Remembrance*, "'charging us to protect those'..." he trailed off expectantly.

"...'with whom we found refuge in our time of need. In this our final duty, we shall not fail,'" Lowella finished begrudgingly before switching topics. "Warm-up? Why would I need a warm-up for a punishment?"

"There will be no punishment. Not today, at least." Dara stepped to the center of the floor and gave Lowella a hard look. "Instead, every moment will be devoted to grappling and submissions." A grin curled the corner of his mouth. "It is unacceptable for my student to merely *try* to break an opponent's arm."

Days passed, and there had been no mention of Lowella's fight. Dara began to hope the entire event would blow over until the morning he awoke to a knock at his door. He opened it to find three civilians, who he invited into his room.

First to enter was Lavonne, a medtech and the first person he met during their journey. Her usually soft and caring face was shadowed by seriousness and concern.

Next was Steven Sarsfield, the leader of the refugee camp. His engineering background and levelheadedness had made him an invaluable member of the community as they transformed this abandoned mining facility into a livable safehouse. Dara did not know the last one to enter, a short woman with a bob cut and stern blue eyes.

"Dara, you remember Steven," Lavonne said as the door slid shut behind the group. "And this is Dr. Arley Dammann, head of infrastructure." She gestured to the other woman, prompting a courteous nod from Dara.

"I can explain." Dara seized the initiative with his planned speech to justify Lowella's fight. "The provocation was intentional, and the response was in line with our customs."

Confusion washed over the others as they exchanged questioning glances.

"I don't know what you're going on about, Dara, but we've come to ask for your help." Lavonne looked to Steven.

"Yesterday, we detected a jump signature. This morning we picked up an inbound DropShip estimated at ten days from planetfall." Steven raised an open hand, forestalling any questions. "No, it isn't the *Dog Leg*. We must assume the *Dog Leg* is still searching for the rest of the Hounds. We haven't received any messages from the unknown ship yet, but as we're the only people on this dead rock, we have to assume they're coming here for us."

"Could it be the Falcons? Did they follow us?" Dr. Dammann's voice betrayed no fear, but carried a sharp edge.

"It would be irrelevant," Dara answered, shaking his head. "If it is the Jade Falcons, not even pulling back into the mines would protect us from the amount of firepower they could muster, and the weapons and explosives your Hounds hid here would do little against them. But the Falcons would not remain silent during their approach. It is not their way."

Steven nodded. "That was my thought, too. So then, who else would be coming here?"

Lavonne raised a hand. "Someone like us, with a safehouse or supplies stockpiled here, bandits, scroungers, people hunting us for good or ill," she said, counting off the list on her fingers.

"If it's someone looking to provide us support, I doubt they would hesitate to communicate. Scroungers or people tapping a hidden depot would probably want to avoid us, so they're not of concern." Steven looked at the group to confirm his line of thinking. "So we're left with bandits, or some unknown attacking force." He looked up at Dara. "I know you've been doing security training with some of our people over the last several weeks. What do you estimate we could do?"

"Those I have trained show proficiency and commitment, but against a comparably sized regular infantry unit, your losses would be significant. With the advantage of being the defender, I think the complex could be held. If the attackers have combat vehicles or even a single 'Mech—" Dara shook his head. "—there is not enough time to effectively train anti-vehicle or 'Mech tactics. Attacking those types of threats would mean our slaughter."

"If they're pirates, it means they're after something," Lavonne offered. "What if we just give them what they want so they go away?"

"I left my whole life back on Arc-Royal," Dr. Dammann said through a sneer. "Those filthy Falcons took so much from each and every one of us, and I'll be damned if I'm going to give up one more thing to anyone!" She looked the other three in the eye in turn, and no one challenged her. "Besides, if Dara thinks we can fight off infantry, give me the explosives, and I'll take care of anything else that might show up."

Dara shrugged. "Those explosives will only work if placed directly on the armor."

"That's precisely why I brought the good doctor in on this," Steven interrupted. "She has some ideas worth exploring."

"Before coming here, I was a geologist." Dr. Dammann produced maps of the facility and mines from a satchel. "Between the explosives, the billions of liters of irradiated water in the mines, and the structure of the tunnels, I think I could turn the planet itself against anyone looking for a fight."

Surveying the maps, Dara recognized the layout of the complex. Built against the cliff face, where mining operations had started centuries ago, stood the central tower. From the overhead perspective of the map, the complex's seven rows of living quarters radiated out from the tower like ripples on a pond. Connecting the tower to these structures were five walkways sealed against the planet's hostile environment.

"The miners here were greedy," Dr. Dammann said as she held the overlaid maps up to the light. "Looks like they followed a vein anywhere it went and with no oversight." Her finger tapped a spot on the map outside the complex's primary entrance, where the subterranean map revealed a large intersection of tunnels. "They put tunnels throughout the whole valley. With a little pumping and prep, this whole area could be made ready to collapse."

"So, what do you think, Dara?" Steven asked. "Could it work?"

Dara's lips stretched thin with doubt as he mulled the idea. When he finally reached his decision, he nodded cautiously.

"Good, then we have planning to do, and quick." Taking the maps, Steven moved to Dara's small table to begin formulating the logistics.

"You're going to feel a bit of pressure again," Lavonne said in her calming tone, "but on the bright side, you won't feel your knee for a couple of hours." With the warning given, she plunged the needle into Dara's joint for the third time. "Now, be careful. The blocker will keep your knee from slowing you down, but you also won't be able to register any further injury either," she said as she disposed of the syringe. "I'm still not sure how you talked me into this."

"I hope it proves to be an unnecessary precaution," Dara replied. In seconds, any sensation of the unique brace on his leg disappeared. Electric pads from the brace were placed on Dara's skin and helped block pain, and the brace itself would keep the knee supported to allow him to walk without other aid. Lavonne had warned that using it would surely cause catastrophic damage to the joint, but to Dara, it was a reasonable price.

As the pain in his leg subsided, he became acutely aware of the aches and pains he had developed across the rest of his body while preparing defenses over the last several days. He then hoisted himself off the edge of the table and began pulling on his environmental suit.

"Please thank everyone for this," he said as he secured the suit's fasteners. "Making the brace so quickly is no small task."

"No thanks needed. I just hope it doesn't electrocute you," she shot back, which raised a concerned eyebrow from Dara. She flashed a reassuring smile. "Just make sure you get back here. There's a certain girl who needs you, and honestly, I don't think she'd listen to anyone else."

Dara chuckled. "It is sad and humorous if you think that is listening." With his suit buttoned up, he grabbed his equipment belt and helmet.

Lavonne's smile faded. "How do you think this parley will go?"

"With the little we know, it is impossible to say. Sending us a message minutes after landing and asking for a meeting seems odd."

"I don't trust it."

"I do not believe anyone does," Dara said over his shoulder as he approached the door. "Which is why we are taking precautions."

"Dara, good luck."

He turned back just enough to nod, and left the central hub to meet up with the other defenders. A few minutes into the journey, he realized he had picked up a tail. He stopped and silently counted to three to give her a chance to analyze the situation. Everything could be a lesson.

"How did you know?" Lowella's voice came from a shadow.

"I have trained young warriors for decades," he said as he turned. "Hearing the lightest of footsteps was a necessary skill. You have something you wish to discuss, *quiaff*?"

"*Aff*. I want to join the defenders. I have more training than almost everyone else combined. You always remind me that I am Clan, and I am a warrior. So why have me stand aside now, with a possible fight coming?"

"There are multiple reasons," Dara said with an introspective sigh, "some of which you might not understand or appreciate. I know you would conduct yourself well if fighting broke out, but it is not the best place for you." He scratched his short beard as he considered how to best explain in a way the young warrior would accept. "When the great ilKhan, Ulric Kerensky, split our Clan a century ago, what became of the Khans?"

"Khan Natasha Kerensky joined him to fight the Jade Falcons, and saKhan Phelan Kell shepherded the Wardens in their new home in the Inner Sphere," Lowella answered by rote.

"Correct," Dara solemnly replied as he set down his helmet and began adjusting the Magnum auto-pistol and combat knife on his weapon belt. "This decision was based on the Khans' political views, knowledge of the Inner Sphere, or combat ability?"

"*Neg*," she shook her head. "Both were Wardens with history in the Inner Sphere and were exceptional warriors." Lowella's eyes darted back and forth as she processed the question.

"You are forgetting about time," Dara prompted.

"Do you mean, because I am younger, I do not have the opportunity to fight?" Lowella's nose wrinkled. "That is not the way of the Clans."

Dara chuckled. "I am aware of our customs, Lowella. I am saying the Khan fought their present battle, and the saKhan was selected to fight the battle of the future. I believe we find ourselves in a similar situation with these civilians. If hostilities break out, it is my duty to fight this battle, but I am certain your greatest value will be in the future. Your current duty is to stay with the noncombatants and be their guardian."

He completed the alterations to his weapon belt and slung it over Lowella's shoulder like a bandolier. The heavy pistol and spare magazine hung under her left arm, and the knife angled across her back. "If anyone makes it past the rest of us, it will be up to you to defend the others. Remember your fundamentals. Be prepared for the recoil."

They shared a silent moment, but Dara could see concern growing in Lowella's eyes and spoke before she could voice it. "Now go, before they seal you outside the control tower."

Lowella paused for a moment before she turned on her heel and hustled back down the corridor. Dara quietly watched her go, his brow furrowed with worry of his own. He took a long slow breath, chastising himself for not telling her the truth. *I watched my Clan's future burn on Arc-Royal. I cannot bear losing her as well.*

A short, painless walk brought him to one of the mess halls where a few dozen people stood in environmental suits in the reds and blacks of the Kell Hounds. They surrounded a table strewn with maps where Steven was working through the defensive strategy for what was likely the hundredth time that day.

"Sensors are picking up the same single BattleMech and three armor units that unloaded here last night," Steven said as he traced a circle on the map with his finger. "They're about twenty-five kilometers out. We can only assume they will approach through here." He drew his finger to the valley opening that led to the mines. "And they'll bring all their heavy equipment. Whether for self-defense during the parley or for intimidation, we'll have to wait and see. If things do go hot, our goal is to get the 'Mech and armor into the kill zone indicated by the red square. We radio Dr. Dammann, and she takes care of them." He emphasized the point with a fist dropped onto the marked area on the map. "Then we clean up any infantry that makes it into the outer rings of the facility. Bear in mind, if they show up with a jumping 'Mech or hover armor, we need to make them primary targets. Questions?"

All heads shook.

"Good, then take a minute to organize your things and get ready to take positions."

Everyone left the table and busied themselves with last-minute preparations. Dara waved over a couple of other members of the squad to assist him in donning the bulky chest and back rigs that formed a support harness. After securing them in place, they slid a heavy ammo can into its mount on his back and lifted his weapon out of its storage case. Dara maneuvered the articulating arm on the front of his harness into the mounting point of the man-portable autocannon. Finally, they helped him feed the belt of rounds from the pack to the cannon. A flip of a switch set the triple barrels to whirring and aligned the first round on the feed ramp. Dara thanked the two for their help and powered down the cannon.

Steven's personal communicator chirped, and he acknowledged a short message. "Okay, everyone!" he shouted. "Scans are showing they're on the move. Take your posts. Nonessential power will be cut in two minutes."

The group dispersed, both nerves and determination evident in their movements.

Dara pulled on his helmet and closed the neck ring, automatically engaging the suit's air supply. He walked through two compartments, sealing the automated doors behind him, and headed up a flight of stairs.

At the top, he opened a trapdoor and walked onto the roof of the prefab living quarters. The overcast skies blocked nearly all the light from the system's star. This alone would have given a sense of twilight, but some form of pollution in the clouds imparted a dark purple glow to the entire heavens, a stark difference to the orangish-red of the surface's sandy ground.

Several dirt-filled barrels lined the roof's edge, and Dara slid behind them. Looking across the compound, he could see other volunteers taking similar hidden positions. From there, they would have clear fields of fire with their heavy weapons, while defenders with lighter weapons were lying in wait in carefully hidden foxholes. Their job was to act as quick response forces should the enemy give an exterior push toward the command tower where the noncombatants were secured, along with every bit of useful supplies not bolted down. If this turned into a shooting match, the hope was to drive any attackers inside, where the sealed bulkheads would slow their advance. Of course, the plans hinged on the belief any potential attackers would be after supplies, hopefully deterring them from blasting the whole complex to pieces.

Dara settled into the most comfortable position he could manage while wearing the bulky harness. Alone in his thoughts, he felt his palms begin to sweat inside his suit, and his heart accelerated until his pulse was a steady thrumming he could feel across his entire body. He breathed slowly and flexed his hands, trying to fight back the dread. The rhythmic rumbles of 'Mech footsteps snapped him back to the present.

"Okay, everyone, stand by. They're coming into view," Steven's voice crackled to all the Kell Hounds. "Stay calm, and we'll all get through this."

Dara peeked between gaps in his cover to spy an approaching BattleMech. Its dorsal laser, long torso, and wide stance were easily identifiable. The *Hussar* was an ancient model, well known for its speed, minimal armor, and lack of antipersonnel weapons. Its large-bore laser was not suited for attacking infantry or buildings. Its greatest threat here would be its fists and feet.

Any feeling of optimism quickly evaporated as two Prowler tracked infantry carriers and a generic-looking APC hovercraft crested the rise at the mouth of the canyon. To make matters worse, the *Hussar* took up a position to the right of the prepared kill zone and stood menacingly while the slower vehicles finished their approach. Each Prowler carried enough close-range firepower to easily overwhelm their small band of foot troops.

A pop in Dara's headset cut through his racing thoughts.

"Broadcasting in the clear, let's have a parley," Steven said as he and a few bodyguards walked out from the complex. They stopped at the edge of the area Dr. Dammann had set for the trap, making themselves both the envoy and bait.

"Left flank," Dara said into his helmet mic, making sure he was broadcasting on the encrypted channel, "can anyone covertly take a position to lure that 'Mech into the kill zone?"

A few disembodied affirmatives came back, and Dara returned his attention to the coming negotiation.

The Prowlers took up flank positions as the APC glided between them and did a slow drift to bring it perpendicular to the welcoming group before it reduced power to the fans and settled on its belly. The side door released and lowered, and a half-dozen people in environmental suits filed out. The first five took positions in a crescent, scanning the area with their long guns at the ready. They settled into relaxed poses, and the sixth stepped between them with a careless flair and approached the band of Hounds civilians.

Steven stood with his hands on his hips and projected a firm tone. "I am the chosen representative of this settlement. The name is Steven. What brings you and your war machines to our door?"

"You can call me Gill," the other man replied over the same open channel as he took a step closer. "As for why I'm here, well, I thought that'd be obvious. Heard rumors there were power signatures on this old dust ball and thought we'd come check it out."

"Well, as you can see, there is nothing here but some refugees," Steven said as he gestured with open hands toward the complex behind him. "It doesn't look like you're prepared to provide aid, so I think it would be best if you just accepted facts and went about your way."

"Sorry, friend," Gill answered, his reflective helmet shaking back and forth. "It just doesn't work that way. You see, my people came looking for some treasure, and how do you think they'll feel if I tell them we can't get any salvage because some sorry war orphans won't let us have it?"

"What business arrangements you have with your people is none of my—"

"I don't have time for this," Gill interrupted.

On cue, the loading doors on the Prowlers unsealed. The pops and hisses of air escaping from the pressurized compartments were loud enough to distract the envoys. It was all the time Gill needed.

Faster than anyone could react, he pulled an auto-pistol from the back of his belt and fired once, slumping Steven where he stood. Gill's escort quickly followed suit, firing needler rifles and shotguns into the three guards, dropping them before they could defend themselves. Time became a slow crawl as the gunshots echoed back and forth between the steep cliffs surrounding the complex.

"Fire!" Dara shouted into his mic as he rose and pushed one of the barrels off the roof to give himself a corridor of fire with the waist-level autocannon. As he engaged the weapon's electrical systems, the other heavy-weapon positions also came to life. "Hit the blower with everything you have! Left side, draw that 'Mech to the kill zone, now!"

In a second, the quiet hole on a dead planet erupted into hell incarnate. Coherent beams of laser light and tracer rounds spiderwebbed between the complex and the vehicles. Foot troopers poured from the Prowlers, rushing for the main entrance, firing at anyone they saw. The *Hussar* stepped forward and slammed a fist down into the nearest rooftop emplacement. One defender managed to escape by leaping headlong from the roof, but there had been at least three people posted there. Screams and unintelligible shouting filled the comms as the chaos of battle washed over the defenders.

Dara streamed shells at the APC, but his projectiles ricocheted off the vehicle's armor and into the dim sky. One of the portable lasers added to the attack and cut a gash in the air skirt under the driver compartment.

"Do I set it off?" Dammann, her voice tight with stress in Dara's ear, cut through the pandemonium and the sudden squelch of interference.

"No, not yet!" Dara shouted back. Though the mic was only millimeters from his mouth, the constant roar of shells from the spinning barrels of his autocannon made shouting the only way to be heard. "Left flank, fire on that 'Mech or we are *done*!" he ordered, not knowing if there was anyone left to hear it.

The containers serving as Dara's small fortress rang as antiperson-nel rounds ripped into their far side. Dara kept his trigger depressed and shifted the autocannon on its hydraulic arm. Projectiles snaked through the air as he moved his aim to the open ramp on the left-hand Prowler. A grisly scowl crossed his face as his stream of tracer rounds rattled and danced inside the vehicle.

Finally, the repositioned flank made their presence known. The green beam of their laser flashed from a pile of tailings far to the left. The beam lasted for only a moment but left a glowing orange scar running vertically on the *Hussar*'s torso as proof of its brief existence. The 'Mech paused just as it was about to swat another emplacement and turned toward the new nuisance.

"We can't wait while people die!" Dr. Dammann's voice came across the comm as the 'Mech pivoted and took its first step to the left. "I don't care what you say. We need to—"

"Now, Doctor. *Now*!" Dara barked.

A moment passed. Then, like rolling thunder from an underground storm, a deep rumble started at Dara's feet and slowly built until it carried through his entire body. He leaned against a barrel to maintain his balance as the vibrations grew into shaking and watched as their trap snapped shut on the pirates.

The earth in front of the primary entrance, where Steven had intentionally drawn the vehicles, began to dance. As the deep rumbling continued, the Prowlers attempted to accelerate away from the shifting ground, but the motion of their tracks only accelerated the earth crumbling beneath them. Both Prowlers disappeared into the gritty soil as if devoured by a hungry planet.

The APC's engines roared up to full power as the driver tried to rise above the danger, but the hovercraft's nose drooped due to the damaged lift skirt. It managed half a meter of lift in the tail, but the skirt could not hold the fans' pressure, blasting everything within twenty meters with high-speed rocks. The driver kept revving the lift fans, and the vehicle slowly drifted in slow circles around its nose, unable to level out.

The running *Hussar* attempted to avoid the forming sinkhole, but the erratic APC twirled into its path and smashed into the *Hussar*'s leg midstride. The scream of grinding armor plates deafened as the 'Mech toppled over and crushed the hovercraft before skidding into the flowing dirt. As the rumbling died down and the earth settled back into a solid, the *Hussar* was buried up to its head, its arms and legs helplessly locked in the ground.

"Doline complete," Dammann called over the hissing comms. "Did we get them?"

Dara began to reply, but stopped as the *Hussar*'s laser activated. In an act of vengeance for the earlier damage, the 'Mech pumped countless megajoules into the rock pile the laser squad was using as concealment. Superheated stone exploded, steel melted, and flesh flashed into steam.

For the second time in as many minutes, the calm was shattered. Every Hound in sight of the *Hussar* fired at it until one of the lasers blazed across the ferroglass canopy. The 'Mech spasmed before going limp, a telltale sign of a sudden disconnection from the MechWarrior's neurohelmet inputs.

A stream of gunfire ripped a line of holes in Dara's cover, forcing him to step out of view. After a few breaths, he returned to his overwatch position and glimpsed the now-abandoned enemy infantry. Clouds of flechettes, rifle rounds, and rolling flame filled the air. The last caused the bile to rise in Dara's throat. He had heard of *dezgra* raiders using portable flamers to attack sealed habitats like the mining complex, but the thought of these attackers going through compartment by compartment, burning the oxygen out of each as they went, was too much to fathom. It brought to mind images of suffocating civilians and caused his vision to cloud.

He spun up his autocannon and began pouring shells toward the attackers. The autocannon was never meant as an antipersonnel weapon, but its shells battered support beams, metal walls, and stone piles until they found their targets on the other side. One raider carrying a flamer tried to break from cover, but autocannon rounds passed through flesh as easily as Albion's tainted air and pierced the flamer's fuel tank, igniting its contents. A fireball billowed into the indigo sky and acted as an exclamation point of the battle. The surviving attackers began throwing their weapons away and raising their empty hands in the universal sign of surrender.

Some of the Hounds civilians took cautious steps toward the raiders, keeping their weapons trained on them as they barked orders over the open frequencies. Other defenders cheered, while yet others sobbed. Interspersed throughout were calls for assistance. It seemed determination and a fair amount of luck had carried the civilians to a costly victory.

The headset crackled through an electric hum. "Dara, this is Dammann."

"I read you. What do you need, Doctor?"

"Might be nothing, but could you give a look at Corridor Two? Control says power was restored to it, but its systems are haywire."

Dara crossed the roof to get a clear view of the next corridor over. From the outside, everything appeared quiet, but an uneasy feeling gnawed at him.

"What malfunctions are you registering?" he asked.

"One sec," Dammann replied before the mumbling of distant voices filled the comm as she spoke with someone else in the control room. "Looks like some sort of cascading issue involving atmo and thermo. Maybe lift and door controls. Hard to say for sure, but Corridor Two did take a bad hit from that 'Mech, from the looks of it."

"Wait, you said 'cascading'? Which area is currently affected?"

"It started at Ring Seven and is currently causing failures at Rings Two and Three. Why?"

Dara stared at the buildings, trying to place the source of his unease. His eyes widened in panic as he realized he had heard the buzz in his headset before. Once, decades earlier, his communicator had been affected by hostile electronics causing similar interference.

"That is not a malfunction, Doctor. It is an attack!" Dara snarled. "They had another force! This was a distraction!"

His eyes darted across the prefabs making up the second corridor and saw no way he could gain immediate access. He pulled the quick release on his harness, and the autocannon and ammo box fell at his feet with a resonant *thud*. His best hope was to beat the attackers to the hub.

He crossed the tops of the buildings and sealed hallways in the loping run only possible in reduced gravity and willed his knee to stay intact with the impact of every step. He was so busy silently cursing himself for not seeing the stealthy assault for what it was he barely registered the rest of the civilians rallying to pursue the intruders as well.

Dara arrived at the airlock on the second level of the control tower and punched a code into the keypad beside it. The door slowly slid open, and once inside, he hit the cycle button. The wait for the door to seal and pump out the poison air seemed like an eternity, and he paced like a tiger in a very small cage. Finally, the interior door was released. He rushed through it and hurried down the hallway to a conference area. He barged through the door, and several children shrieked. Between him and the noncombatants stood Lavonne, a heavy pipe gripped in a white-knuckled fist and an electric intensity in her eyes, which softened when she recognized Dara.

"They are coming," he said bluntly as he looked among the assembled children. "Where is Lowella?"

Lavonne opened her mouth to respond, but a series of gunshots echoed through the metal building. Her eyes looked past Dara to the source of the gunshots, and he had his answer.

Without a second thought, he spun and darted out of the room and down the hall. A few short, tight corridors later, he arrived at the ladder access to the lower level. Flinging open the hatch cover, he was overcome by black, oily smoke that spilled up out of the darkness below. Dara leaped blindly into the opening, caught himself on the sides of the ladder, and slid to the floor. He activated the flashlight mounted to his helmet, but even its powerful beam struggled to cut through the haze.

Dara stumbled forward in the dark, and a glint of metal on the floor caught his eye. Bending to pick it up, he recognized an empty magazine from his auto-pistol. He found the pistol itself a step farther into the compartment, its slide locked back on an empty magazine. His own breath in his helmet felt thunderous as he searched for his ward. Then the smoke swirled apart for a moment, and he saw her.

A pipe angled from the wall and jammed the door that separated Corridor Two from the tower. Dara's combat belt was looped around it, and hanging lifelessly in the belt was Lowella.

As he neared the bulkhead, he could see the marks from a half-dozen large slugs and realized Lowella had fought back the attackers here. The pipe was propped in a way that would prevent the door from opening, and she had used her own weight to keep it secured, even as the air smoldered around her.

Dara raced to her and lifted her from the belt, cradling her in his massive arms. He brushed singed hair from her face, wiped the smudges of soot from under her nose, and fumbled to find a pulse through the gloves of his suit.

Images of the burning genetic repository during the fall of Arc-Royal rushed unbidden through his mind, and his faith faltered, just as it had that day. A gasp from behind him shook away his reverie, and he turned to find Lavonne wearing a breathing regulator and goggles. He feebly held Lowella's form out to her.

"Save her," he said softly, the words barely carrying beyond his helmet. "You must." He hoped the smoke kept Lavonne from seeing the shame that had overtaken him. "Go. Seal the hatch behind you."

A metallic *bang* from the door made Lavonne flinch, and with a determined nod, she lifted Lowella from Dara's arms and hoisted her over a shoulder. She turned and retreated toward the ladder.

Dara watched them disappear into the smoke when a second jarring *clang* rang out from the door. He slowly turned to his belt and drew his knife from its sheath. Gripping the handle, he tested the blade's weight and silently vowed he would exact justice. The realization that Lowella might not awaken to learn of his deeds sent a shudder across his shoulders. He clenched his jaw so hard he felt his teeth might splinter, and turned off his flashlight.

Standing alone in the dark, he grappled his worries one at a time and drowned them in a sea of wrath. *If I have failed her, then this blood will be for me.*

Behind him, he heard Lavonne dogging the hatch, followed by a few moments of silence. With a casual flick of his foot, he popped the pipe free from where it was pinned. It clattered loudly on the floor as he silently waited beside the doorway. The manual-operation lever on the door crept up, and the door slowly slid open. He had spent most of his life training others in close quarters and hand-to-hand combat. This was to be his master class.

Smoke flowed out through the open portal, and the telltale pilot flame of a portable flamer entered. Dara pressed himself against the wall as three long gouts of flame filled the room and lit the thick smoke from within, casting a surreal glow. Dara's atmo suit protected him from the heat, and just as the flamer began to withdraw, Dara sprang.

He grabbed the flamer with his free hand and pulled with every fiber of his muscled frame. The trooper left their feet as they sailed through the air, and with a quick pivot, Dara spun and smashed them headfirst into the wall. The force of the impact shattered the trooper's visor, and the suit's overpressure blasted the broken glass away. A quick yank severed the air hose from the helmet, and Dara twisted the man around to pin his back to the wall.

With the flamer trapped harmlessly between them, Dara delivered a vicious knee to the man's diaphragm, forcing the air from his lungs. He watched as the terror flashed in the intruder's widening eyes at the realization that he had, just seconds before, burned away the precious oxygen in the room. As the man took a breath of the dead air, a part of Dara nearly felt pity, but the memory of Lowella in his arms was too fresh, and the feeling died before it could take hold.

Letting the unconscious man slide to the floor, Dara turned back to the door. Apparently, with little honor among pirates, at least a few of the man's companions had decided to shoot blindly into the darkness, heedless of their comrade's safety. As the impotent gunshots trickled to a stop, Dara fired the pillaged flamer across the doorway's opening.

"Anyone who passes through this door will be burned alive," he called out. The threat gave the invaders pause, and Dara took a moment to cut a slit in the now dead pirate's environmental suit. He stuffed the air tube he had ripped free into the hole and then cut the fuel line to the flamer and jammed the loose hose into the suit with the other.

"Everyone, stay clear of Compartment Two-One," he mumbled into his communicator. A series of confused confirmations responded.

"What was that?" an invader called out from beyond the door, mistaking that Dara had said something to them. "Listen, pal, we don't want any trouble here, and this is way more pain than it's worth. So how about you give us back our associate, and we'll be on our way."

"That is a gracious offer," Dara said as he swiftly worked to override the oxygen controls on the deceased pirate's suit and disabled the regulator on the flamer's fuel tank. He checked the manual igniter at the end of the detached gun portion of the flamer to ensure it still worked. "I will accept it, but you must then leave immediately."

"Of course, buddy, I promise."

"Here is your comrade. Now be gone." Dara hefted the body, its suit now filling with a dangerously flammable mixture, and threw it out the door, where it landed with a hollow *thud*. He pivoted away from the door and readied to charge with his knife and igniter.

"Shit! They killed him! You sons of—"

A man stormed through the door, his needler rifle coming up to his shoulder.

Dara knocked the rifle aside with the flamer and planted his feet. He leveled his knife, and the momentum of the man's rush carried him to the hilt of Dara's honed steel.

Hoisting the dying man still on his blade, Dara pushed him back into the doorway to prevent any other attackers from crossing the threshold. Instead of the rush of opponents he expected, Dara saw several raiders a few meters away, barely visible in the smoke.

Motion caught his eye as a fist-sized cylinder flew toward him. Instinctively, he blocked it with the impaled invader, and the grenade bounced back into the corridor. The attackers froze, torn between fleeing and trying to throw it again as it rolled to rest against the body in the middle of the floor.

With no way to tell what sort of grenade he had just deflected, Dara raised the skewered man as a shield when the stun grenade detonated. A flash and thunderous noise heralded the rolling fireball from the mixture of oxygen and flamer fuel igniting.

The fiery blast swept Dara's feet out from under him, and he went sprawling through the air. He landed hard, but kept ahold of his knife. Knowing the environmental suits would protect the pirates from the worst of the flames, he stormed forward with a baritone roar of inconsolable rage. Through the smoke and the spots in his vision, he could barely make out the outline of the door, and dove into the black smoke beyond.

Dara became the heart of bloody chaos. In the madness of the smoke and crisscrossing flashlight beams, he lashed out with his blade at anyone he saw, not burdened by target identification. As weapons leveled at him, he knocked them aside or slammed the wielder down with a blow. Unseen gunshots were followed by pressure warnings from his suit's systems. Somewhere in his mind Dara knew what this meant, but he continued to strike with every motion.

"In this, our final duty, we shall not fail."

The line from *The Remembrance* echoed through his mind as his attacks became even more impetuous. His grip crushed limbs. His fist and feet broke bones. His knife struck true and bit deep time and again, until there were no more pirates fighting against him.

Dara stalked after the last of his prey, a fleeing trooper covered in comm and computer gear, out of the smoke and down the hallway, the invader stumbling away in terror. His eyes narrowed as he realized this one was likely an electronic-warfare specialist, the reason the invaders had been able to make such quick progress through the facility. The reason the civilians and Lowella had been in danger.

The unarmed hacker was clawing at the ground, trying to slide away on his back. Desperately trying to escape his doom, the man backed into a wall. With nowhere else to flee, Dara loomed over him and raised his crimson-covered knife.

"Don't move!" someone shouted.

Dara looked up to see a half-dozen people in the Hounds' environmental suits coming the other direction down the walkway. The hacker scurried toward the Hounds, pleading for surrender. Dara slowly raised his arms out to his sides so they could see he was not a threat and waited for them to recognize him.

"Holy hell... Dara, is that you?"

The shock and concern in the voice made Dara look down to see himself covered in gore. Most was not his, but enough of it was. With the recognition of his wounds, the pain hit him like a charging 'Mech, dropping him to his knees. He collapsed and rolled onto his back as Hounds ran to his side. One knelt beside him and began surveying his injuries. The small shrug and shake of the head they gave those assembled confirmed what Dara already knew.

"Dara," Lavonne's voice said over the communicator, "the shooting stopped. Are you okay?"

"The threat was stopped," he replied. A cough sent a red splatter across the inside of his visor. "How is Lowella?"

"She woke up once she got into clean air. She'll be okay, I think."

"Put her on."

"She should rest—" Lavonne began to protest.

"Please..." he said, the plea raw in his voice.

"Dara?" the groggy voice of Lowella asked. "Did you stop them?"

"I did, thanks to you." A proud grin crossed Dara's face before a grimace of pain forced it away. "Time is short, and I must ask something of you." He struggled to take a breath. "I am *solahma*, unworthy of *The Remembrance*, but it would be enough if *you* would remember me." His body was wracked with another series of wheezing coughs. "Will you?"

"*Seyla*," was the immediate reply, the last thing Dara heard before the world faded to an infinite dark.

"Hello, Dara," Lowella began with a slight tremble in her voice as she stood at the base of the cliff. "I came to tell you the *Dog Leg* returned. They found a trail back to the rest of the Kell Hounds, so we will be going to join them once the last of the equipment is loaded. No news about the other Wolves-in-Exile, but Lavonne and Dr. Dammann said we would keep looking."

She took a breath and frowned. "Do you recall our last morning on Arc-Royal? You told me the Khan gave you six months to heal your leg, or you would become a trainer, but it had been pointless. I did the math. If you had been reassigned immediately, you would never have been *my* instructor." She blinked dampness from her hazel eyes. "So, to me, it was not pointless at all. It has meant everything."

She slowly reached out and carefully ran her fingers over Dara's name engraved in the cliff face, a small memorial to those who died in the pirate attack.

"I will remember you," she whispered.

Lowella rose and walked to the excavated and jury-rigged *Hussar*. Fighting the urge to look back, she climbed the chain ladder and slid into the cockpit. After letting the air cycle and donning the neurohelmet, she brought the 'Mech's systems up from standby and opened the comm.

"*Dog Leg*, this is Guardian One. I am on my way."

UNIT DIGEST: STEEL WOLVES

ALEX FAUTH

Affiliation: Mercenary
CO: Star Colonel Xera
Average Experience: Veteran/Reliable
Force Composition: 2 BattleMech Trinaries, 1 Vehicle Trinary, 1 Battle Armor/Infantry Trinary, 1 Aerospace Trinary; full DropShip and JumpShip support
Unit Abilities: +1 Initiative when facing Clan opponents. One unit per Star may be rolled on the Wolf Empire RAT.
Parade Scheme: Silvery steel and hide-brown colors. Sometimes crafty technicians add fur patterns to the brown portions of the upper surfaces, to create the overall effect of a steel warrior wearing the pelts of prey animals.

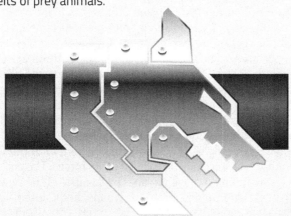

UNIT HISTORY

Originally raised as Republic Prefect Kal Radick's personal army, the Steel Wolves took many twists to bring them to their present existence as a mercenary command. The key moment came in 3135, when Anastasia Kerensky dissolved the force to form the Wolf Hunters, a mercenary command molded in her image. This move was deeply unpopular among many Trueborn Wolves within their ranks, resulting in mass desertions.

The largest group of deserters coalesced under the control of Varnoff Fetladral, who pulled together two Clusters of warriors. Declaring his force the reborn Steel Wolves, he aimed to reclaim Tigress, the unit's homeworld, and the rest of their small empire. While Fetladral claimed to adhere to the tenets of Clan honor, during the unit's operations, he engaged in blatantly dishonorable behavior to achieve his goals. Those who protested were quietly sidelined in favor of his loyalists.

Matters came to a head in 3136 on New Canton. Given an opportunity to avenge his slighted honor, Fetladral challenged Anastasia Kerensky to a Trial of Grievance. However, he planned to betray her and simply kill her and the Wolf Hunters outright. His second, Star Colonel Xera, discovered and publicly exposed his treachery. Declaring him *dezgra,* she took control of the Steel Wolves and abandoned Fetladral and his followers.

Although Xera had purged the Steel Wolves of those treacherous elements, she now lacked a direction. With Tigress absorbed into the Federated Suns, any attempt to reclaim it would be suicidal. Her first solution was to jump back toward the former Prefecture VII region to find a world to claim as their own, while also evading the seemingly inexorable Capellan advance. For the next few years, the Steel Wolves simply wandered from world to world, either trading or raiding for supplies.

This reprieve did not last long, with the region being caught up in both the Spirit Cats' migration and then Operation Hammerfall. With the arrival of Clan Wolf in the region, members of the Steel Wolves saw an opportunity to find their new home. Their efforts at outreach did not go as hoped: the Wolves saw them as *dezgra* bandits, stained by their past. After the Wolves simply killed several Stars of Steel Wolf warriors outright, Xera realized their destiny lay in a different direction.

Swallowing her pride, she offered the Steel Wolves' services as mercenaries, becoming the one thing they had opposed the most. Despite their past, they quickly found employment with the Oriente Protectorate, which was looking to build up its forces. The collapse of the Marik-Stewart Commonwealth and the advance of the Lyrans and Wolves had left Oriente desperate for troops, and Captain-General Jessica Marik was more than willing to overlook the Steel Wolves' past.

While not employed in Operation Homecoming, the Steel Wolves helped stabilize the former MSC region after the reformation of the Free Worlds League. The unit proved reliable, with Xera's own sense of honor leading to honest dealings with her employers and remarkably Clan-like conduct on the battlefield. However, the Steel Wolves did not assume the same of their opponents, and were willing to abandon *zellbrigen* against opponents they did not expect to honor it.

The only stain on their performance came when they were deployed to the Clan Protectorate in expectation of further Clan Wolf aggression. The Steel Wolves found themselves stationed alongside the Spirit Cats' Purifier Cluster, and tensions quickly ramped up between the two groups due to their Clan backgrounds and their shared origins within the Republic. A duel between Angus Drummond and Kyria Wolf (herself a former Spirit Cat) left both warriors badly wounded, and their commanders were forced to step in and segregate the two units.

Despite this, the Free Worlds League Military showed considerable faith in the Steel Wolves. The unit scored decisive victories against the Regulan Hussars on Emris IV and Avior, helping to bring the breakaway state back into the League. In 3152, they were able to avenge themselves against the Purifier Cluster on Stewart, defeating the Spirit Cats unit after they came to reclaim the world for the ilClan. Ironically, in this battle the Steel Wolves were aided by the Thirteenth Regulan Hussars.

Xera has recently learned that Varnoff Fetladral is alive and at large, leading a pirate band known as the Wolfkin Keshik. While she would want nothing more than to take Fetladral down for his dishonor, she also remains bound to her employer's orders.

COMPOSITION

The present-day Steel Wolves bear very little resemblance to the force raised by Kal Radick two decades ago. Less than half of their warriors are Republic-bred Trueborn Wolves, although those Wolves who remain occupy most of the senior positions. The rest of the unit's ranks are made up of mercenaries hired over the last decade to make up losses. Those hired into the Steel Wolves are afforded the respect due to a warrior, but are in turn expected to conduct themselves in an honorable manner. Should the opportunity present itself, Xera seeks to claim actual Wolf Empire warriors as bondsmen to strengthen the Clan presence within the unit.

Drawing on its Clan roots, the Steel Wolves is a Cluster organized into Trinaries, and employs Clan ranks. Like their personnel, the unit's equipment has been drawn from a variety of sources. A few remnants of their original Republic Armed Forces equipment can be found among Regulan salvage and materiel purchased on the mercenary market.

Due to their history and the background of their leaders, the Steel Wolves are intimately familiar with Clan tactics, specifically those used by the Wolves. While Xera prefers to lead the Cluster from her *Scytha* OmniFighter, she often commands operations from their flagship, the *Titan*-class *Roofvogel.*

DEATH TO MERCENARIES: RHETORIC VS. REALITY

ERIC SALZMAN

—**Major Brunhilda Gantor,** *Merc Life* editorial, May 3151

Communication is a highly refined art in the Draconis Combine. Epitomized by subtlety and nuance, small gestures, facial expressions, and voice tones carry volumes of meaning to those who know how to read the signs. The consequence of this cultural tradition, however, is that something stated publicly may be parsecs away from the truth.

Consider the case of the Draconis Combine's infamous "Death to Mercenaries" edict. In 3028, Coordinator Takashi Kurita dispatched four regiments to ensure the destruction of Wolf's Dragoons following Jaime Wolf's public upbraiding of him at the Steiner-Davion wedding on Terra. As the fighting raged, Takashi suffered a mild stroke that left him physically debilitated and increasingly paranoid. In December 3028, he issued orders through the Internal Security Force that *all* mercenaries, not just Wolf's Dragoons, should be given no quarter on the battlefield and executed whenever captured.

The orders repulsed many Combine unit commanders, who saw it as a violation of the samurai code of honor. Though such executions had been endorsed as official policy in the Dictum Honorium, the catastrophic collapse in the Draconis Combine Mustered Soldiery's morale after the Kentares Massacre had left such edicts as merely words on paper, rarely referenced, much less enforced during the Succession Wars. Takashi's father, Hohiro, had been assassinated after attempting to reinstate such behavior in the DCMS through his Dragon Renewals. Court observers and field commanders alike speculated that a new wave of Dragon Renewals might be in the offing, and worried that Takashi was following his father's footsteps.

The greater impact, however, was that Takashi's public edict targeting mercenaries also inflamed anti-mercenary passions among the Combine's general populace and encouraged independent actions by local officials hoping to curry favor with the Chrysanthemum Throne. Supposedly "spontaneous" demonstrations (akin to those aimed at the Dragoons during their final year of their service to the Combine) arose around mercenary cantonments on Combine worlds as civilians targeted mercenaries with protests and vandalism. Seeing the writing on the wall, units like McGee's Cutthroats activated their early-escape clauses and left Combine service, while those captured by Lyran advances, such as Helmut's Hermits, opted to not seek repatriation.

When word came in October 3029 that Wolf's Dragoons had triumphed on Crossing, forcing the battered Galedon Regulars to retreat, the enraged Coordinator expanded his earlier "Death to Mercenaries" order to mandate that the Combine would no longer tolerate any mercenary force within its territory. High Command abolished the Professional Soldiery Liaison office, and a mass exodus of mercenaries ensued, with the ISF arresting and executing members of units that failed to extract by 1 January 3030. While prestigious regiments, such as the Tooth of Ymir and the Lone Star Regiment, were able to find new contracts outside the Combine, smaller units struggled to survive the postwar peace.

By the end of the Fourth Succession War, the Combine's purge of mercenaries was complete, lasting until House Kurita rescinded "Death to Mercenaries" in 3052. Or so the official version goes.

This was, in fact, the case for only a decade. In 3030, ComStar promised subsidized mercenary contracts to Takashi's son, Theodore, in exchange for recognizing Rasalhagian independence. Given Takashi's edicts, this baffling offer suggested that Theodore himself was open to using mercenaries, and would soon seize the role of Coordinator. Despite accepting ComStar's deal, Theodore honored Takashi's ban as his father's Deputy for Military Affairs (*Gunji-no-Kanrei*).

The War of 3039 marked a crucial turning point in Combine-mercenary relations. Unknown to Takashi, *Kanrei* Theodore had dispatched his wife, Tomoe Sakade, to the mercenary hiring hub on Davion-held Le Blanc. There, she recruited several battalions comprised of small units, including ex-Combine mercenaries that had fled in 3029. As part of Operation Orochi, these mercenaries launched an unexpected strike into the Davion rear, which played a decisive role in Hanse Davion's decision to abandon his offensive.

Following the Le Blanc gambit's success, the *Kanrei*, with support from ISF Director Subhash Indrahar, authorized limited resumption of mercenary employment. Theodore ordered the Draconis High Command to reestablish the PSL under the directorship of Kobo Fukuzawa, who filtered all contracts through Matabushi, Inc. as an added safeguard against discovery by Takashi or his hardliner loyalists. Matabushi line-itemized contracted mercenaries simply as "specialists" or "troubleshooters," laundered payments, and coded contract terms in dense legal disclaimers. Per its earlier offer, ComStar subsidized these contracts and listed them at hiring hubs.

Throughout the 3040s, the Combine used this system to hire small mercenary units to garrison lesser worlds, hunt pirates, suppress insurgencies, and launch deniable attacks on the Federated Commonwealth. Several of these units, including Team Venom, the Seventh Hell's Brigade, the Dark Horns, the GoldMiners, Rolling Thunder, and Blue Lightning, ended up in the path of the Clans when they arrived in 3049.

The takeaway, then, is that despite an official and severe ban on mercenaries serving the Combine, the needs of the state and of competing power blocs brought dozens of mercenary units back into Combine service while the policy remained the immutable will of the Coordinator. Given the significant uptick in contracts being offered by the Combine just within the last month, a wise mercenary commander will keep this in mind when considering employment offers. The pay and command rights may be appealing, and the PSL may make many promises about how it values mercenary skill and expertise, but if the interests of House Kurita or an ascendant Warlord demand that mercenaries become scapegoats once more, the working environment could shift quickly and dangerously. Before you sign on with the Combine, make sure your escape clauses are airtight and your exit route is pre-plotted, and learn to read the subtle clues behind the propaganda to see the true face of the Dragon.

WINNING THE BATTLE, LOSING THE WAR

JASON DESOUZA

SECURE LANDING SITE
POMPEY III
MARIAN HEGEMONY
30 MAY 3143
0945 HOURS

Lieutenant Maeve Geans glanced around the small circle of officers while attempting to tame her fiery mane from the brisk wind blowing over the group. As the lowest-ranking officer at this briefing, she wanted to make a good impression.

"Everybody here?" Colonel Lyra Hopkins asked, nodding to the other eight figures standing in the DropShip's shadow. "Good, let's begin."

The commander of the Second Magistracy Highlanders picked up a thin stick next to a rough map sketched in the dirt and pointed it at the largest rock. "Nola, the second largest city on Pompey III, home to almost four million people and the main production facility for Hadrian Mechanized Industries. It's also the home of two cohorts from Legio Four. Reports indicate one is a 'Mech unit and the other is a mix of 'Mechs, armor, and possibly battle armor."

Maeve did the math in her head. A cohort was thirty BattleMechs or vehicles, the Marian Hegemony equivalent to a battalion. Two cohorts could be sixty 'Mechs and vehicles, and potentially more, if the intel reports were off.

Colonel Hopkins pointed the stick at a smaller collection of rocks. "This is our position, two hundred kilometers away. We landed with the intent of drawing the Fourth away from the city and into the open, where our technological and numerical advantages would allow us to sweep through the defenders and onto the prize. An urban battle levels the playing field more than I'd like, but we have our mission, and we will complete it."

She moved the stick to a grouping of smaller sticks. "This is the Valley of Magnus, a series of valleys and dry riverbeds that will allow us to approach the city without being seen. Scouts will recon the area, searching for listening posts or patrols." Her head came up as she looked at all of the officers in turn. "Scouting only, no heroics."

Maeve met her gray, determined eyes and nodded.

Colonel Hopkins pointed to a slim figure in camouflage fatigues. "Commander Warren, your company will deploy here." She drew a line in the sand south of the city and east of their current position. "Your tanks and hovercraft will demonstrate an aggressive posture, drawing attention to yourselves and hopefully pulling defenders out of the city. Commander Mitchell, your company will sit back here—" The ad hoc pointer moved to a spot between the city and their position. "—where your 'Mechs can support Warren if he draws a response from the city. You've got the long-range firepower, so put it to good use."

She dropped the stick and straightened her field jacket. "I cannot stress this enough: this is a raid against the manufacturing center, *not* an invasion. Get in, hit approved targets of opportunity, and get out. Don't do unnecessary damage, but don't hold back if lives are on the line."

The colonel looked up at Maeve again before turning to the small woman to her right. "Captain Dappel, your company will provide security for the DropShips, minus Lieutenant Geans and her recon lance. They will undertake the scouting mission."

Colonel Hopkins' gaze met Maeve's again as she continued. "Lieutenant, this is just a scouting mission, nothing more. Recon the valley and radio back with anything you've found." She ran a hand through her fiery red hair before continuing, "That means I don't want to hear about a running battle. You and your lance are scouts, and that's what this job needs. Is that clear, Lieutenant?"

Maeve nodded. "Perfectly, Colonel."

"Recon element leaves in an hour, everyone else should be ready to go in two. Commander Warren, your force leaves right after the recon element." The colonel grabbed the stick in both hands and snapped in it two, tossing both pieces onto the ground. "Dismissed," she said, and walked away.

Maeve stood there a moment, staring at the sand map. Her thoughts turned to her lance and the people in it, both past and present.

She felt a hand on her shoulder and turned to see Captain Dappel standing there. "Are you okay, Lieutenant?"

"Yeah, I'm fine, Captain," she replied. "Just working out the mission in my head, is all."

"That's the problem, Maeve. You spend too much time in your head. You have to let the past go already." Dappel sighed and shook her head. "Frazer was a messed-up mission from the get-go. We dropped into a bad spot. But I need you to focus on this mission." She pulled on Maeve's shoulder, turning her around so they stood face-to-face. "If you don't feel up to this, I can talk to the colonel and get your lance swapped out. No one will judge you for it."

Maeve shook her head. "I'm good to go, Samantha. I'm just working out how to incorporate the new guy into the lance. He's fresh out of training, and his *Wasp* isn't as effective as Delancy's *Anubis*. It's slower, smaller, and not as impactful at long range."

"You heard the colonel—you better not be shooting at *anything* unless you get shot at first," Dappel said. "Maeve, you're one of the best 'Mech commanders in the whole regiment, everyone knows it. Hopkins has been wanting to promote you for months, but she doesn't want to lose you to another regiment. It's selfish of her, but she trusts your skills. Once this is over, I'll pressure her to get you the promotion you deserve. You're past due for a company of your own." She patted Maeve's shoulder. "Get your lance ready to go, we've got a timetable to keep."

Walking back to the company area, Maeve nodded to a few people, but said nothing. She never said the name out loud anymore. *Frazer.*

It had started out much like this mission, a raid on an enemy world, this one held by the Federated Suns. The Second Highlanders were on a joint mission with elements of the Capellan Confederation, to strengthen ties with allies and get valuable combat experience in low-risk situations. Only it wasn't low risk: the defending forces had been stronger than expected. The Highlanders were heavily bloodied before retreating, and Maeve had fallen into a trap that had cost her the life of one lancemate and scars that still haunted her in the night.

Familiar laughter pulled her attention back to the present. The four 'Mechs of her lance were clustered together at the backside of a DropShip. Two of her pilots had stretched out on the grass, while a third paced back and forth near them. As she approached, she could hear their conversation.

"—won't solve anything," the large man on the ground said. "You just need to sit back and relax for as long as you can. Don't worry—you'll be wishing for a break soon enough."

Maeve smiled, Saunders was a good pilot, but a bit rough around the edges. "He's right, Kelder," she added while wandering over and sitting next to the foot of the *Anubis*. "Relax."

Kelder was the newest pilot in her lance, fresh out of the academy on Canopus IV. His posture changed immediately upon seeing her. He wasn't quite at attention, but it was close. *At least he's not saluting me anymore.*

Across from Maeve, Hideo Tomoko propped herself up on an elbow. "What's the mission, LT?" Her soft voice matched her small ebony frame. The *Raven* pilot was *always* the first to ask about the mission, but her singlemindedness and her 'Mech's advanced sensors had contributed to her well-earned nickname of "Bloodhound."

"Simple scouting mission," Maeve said. "Bravo Company gets to watch the fireworks again. Recon goes in and scouts the main route of attack while Striker and Command Lances guard the LZ." She leaned back against the *Anubis'* foot and stretched, trying not to yawn as she glanced down at the chrono strapped to her wrist. "We move out in forty-five minutes. Load up, and expect at least twelve hours in your cockpit. Kelder, you should rest a bit because you're on ration detail. If you bring back any of the spaghetti ones, I'm kicking you out of the lance."

As Maeve ran a hand along the armored foot of her *Phoenix Hawk*, her eyes picked out the small imperfections in the metal. Divots too small to fill, little jagged edges along the seams—those were the things that made it unique, made it special. The fresh camo paint job did little to hide the bigger items, like the replacement armor welded over the hole in its chest, the tiny rust ring on the leg actuator cover.

The stencil on the left side of the head, just under the cockpit sensors, read LT. MAEVE GEANS. Under her name, MINERVA was handwritten in white paint. The unit insignia on the right shoulder featured an eagle with wings extended and a planet between them. Under it was the numeral 1 followed by a capital *B*, a dash, and a capital *R*: Bravo Company, Recon Lance, First Battalion. It was her 'Mech, but she wasn't the first Geans to pilot it. Her mother had piloted it years ago, when she was a member of the Magistracy Armed Forces, and had given the 'Mech its name. It had taken a lot of requests and every favor she could muster from the techs, but she had managed to get it repaired and battle ready. The Magistracy would have restored it eventually, as these trying times didn't allow anyone the luxury of letting BattleMechs rot. She had scored high enough out of the academy for a better 'Mech, but she wouldn't have traded *Minerva* for any other 'Mech in the galaxy.

Maeve checked her HUD again as she advanced into the valley. The terrain was surprisingly smooth for something made by shifting tectonic plates. Her concern was mostly centered on the forests on either side of the valley.

"Heads up, people," she told her lance. "This looks like a perfect ambush spot. Tomoko, take point, but go slow and keep that Beagle probe at max detection. Kelder, you're next, but go slow. Watch where you put each foot, and keep an eye on your HUD. Saunders, fall back just a bit, but be ready to let loose with your missiles if needed."

She watched the *Raven* advance in an almost graceful manner, followed closely by Kelder's *Wasp*. She stepped *Minerva* forward slowly, not bothering to see if Saunders' *Anubis* was moving, as he was one of the best soldiers she had ever met. His discipline in the cockpit was matched only by his lax discipline outside of battle.

As the 'Mechs slowly moved through the valley, Kelder in his *Wasp* impressed her as he managed to step lightly and almost exactly in the tracks Tomoko's *Raven* left.

"Good work, Kelder," Maeve said. "We'll make a scout out of you yet."

The lance took longer than expected to fully scout out the valley system, but it was clear of all Hegemony forces. It worried her just a little that the Marians had left this way into the city completely clean of any outposts or pickets.

Maeve toggled her comm unit to the regimental frequency and said a single word: "Clear." Her fingers deftly toggled back to her lance frequency. "Recon Lance, head back to Waypoint Six."

On her sensors, Maeve watched the main body of the Second Highlanders move into the valley system. Her lance had been spread out on both sides of the valley to watch for any possible enemy movement. She hoped the lack of any enemy signatures was due to the hard work of Commander Warren's task force.

Maeve drummed her fingers on her command couch's armrest as she watched the column of BattleMechs move down the valley. "Highlander Six, One Bravo Recon here," she said, using a tight-beam signal as she saw Colonel Hopkins' distinctive *Highlander* moving past her position. "Do you want us to push ahead of the main body and provide advance reconnaissance?"

"That's a negative, One Bravo Recon," came the reply she knew she would get. "Link back up with One Bravo at the DropShip." The colonel paused and said, "You did great work today, Lieutenant. When this is all over, you and I will have to sit and have a chat about your future in the regiment."

The last of the 'Mechs passed by, and Maeve sighed. The fight was on, and she was on the sidelines.

"One Bravo Six, this is One Bravo Recon," she transmitted to Captain Dappel. "The parade has passed us. Permission to hold position for the time being, to ensure there are no surprises following the column?"

"Granted, One Bravo Recon—as long as you stay in place. No freelancing on this mission. Understood?"

A smile crossed Maeve's lips as she heard the reply. Captain Dappel wasn't against flexibility from her subordinates.

"Copy that. We will keep watch on the back door just in case. No heroics." Maeve switched channels to her lance frequency. "Okay, folks, we are going to stay here a bit and watch the rear. Tomoko, use your bloodhound instincts and find us a good place to hunker down."

The sounds of battle echoed off the valley walls around the 'Mechs of Recon Lance. Maeve sat with her legs hanging out of the cockpit door as she ate a ration pack. Her lance had been in place for almost four hours now, listening to the symphony of the battle. The radio constantly chirped in the cockpit behind her, the regimental channel alive with battle chat. She zoned most of it out, picking up only on key communications.

"Kelder, how long have you been with the lance now?" Saunders asked, his voice echoing softly off his cockpit walls.

The young voice that replied still seemed alien to Maeve, even though he wasn't that new anymore. "Almost six months."

There was a sharp whistle over the comm, followed by a chuckle. "Six months. Boss. Don't you think it's time to give young Kelder here a nickname? 'New guy' is gonna run its course soon enough."

Maeve laughed at that, pulling herself fully into the cockpit again. "You got a suggestion, Saunders, or are you just making small talk?" she replied as she strapped herself back into the chair. The neurohelmet firmly back on her shoulders, she felt the familiar moment of disorientation as her sense of balance began to filter into the 'Mech's diagnostic computer. "Because if I remember correctly, you got your nickname for all of the wrong reasons."

"I've been meaning to ask why that is, the whole nickname thing," Kelder's squeaky voice said.

"It's military tradition, plain and simple," Maeve answered. "Usually, within a few months of being in the unit, you'll do something that gets you a nickname, be it good or bad."

"Do you really think Tomoko would want her family to know her work nickname is 'Bloodhound'?" Saunders added, laughing into the comm.

Maeve laughed again as she watched the explosions in the distance. If not for the destruction, it would have been a beautiful view. The waning light of the day hid much from her line of sight, but the many fires in the city allowed her to follow the regiment's advance.

It was as beautiful as it was deadly—and she wanted to be right in the middle of it.

Several massive explosions rocked the city in succession. Even at the distance she was at, Maeve could feel the rumble the blasts caused. Looking down at her sensors, she toggled through the various regimental channels, trying to figure out what was going on. The panic in some of the voices was apparent, then static filled the channel. Whoever was in charge of the defense must have started jamming their comms.

"All right kids, button up," Maeve transmitted to her lance. "It looks like the party is getting out of hand. It sounds like the Hegemony forces have rigged some of the buildings with explosives."

"One Bravo Recon, this is One Bravo Six. What the hell is going on over there?"

"Six, things look chaotic from where we are," Maeve replied. "There's too much smoke to see anything clearly, and comms are jammed. I've lost all contact with everyone from the assault force."

"Understood. Move forward and secure the route out. Don't get into a fight if you can avoid it, and for God's sake, do *not* go into that city. Hold the door open, and see if you can use Tomoko's *Raven* to get word to anyone in the city."

The outskirts of the city showed minor damage, but destruction seemed to grow the deeper Maeve looked into the maze of buildings. Her lance had advanced to the edge of the city and spread out in a line along the base of the last hill. Tomoko's *Raven* was as far forward as it could be without actually entering the city proper.

"Saunders," Maeve said, "find a good spot for your missiles, and be ready to fire if a target presents itself. Kelder, stay close to Saunders and watch his back. Tomoko, see if your ECM can break through this jamming. We've had a mistake-free day so far, let's try to keep it that way."

Maeve toggled through the Highlanders' comm channels, and while she got small snippets of comm traffic, a lot of it was garbled and static-filled. *Why have none of the other ECM-equipped 'Mechs in the regiment toggled their ECM to cut through this?*

Explosions lit up the darkening sky again as Recon Lance sat at the edge of the city. Tracer rounds and stray energy beams lanced into the night, reminding Maeve of a fireworks display she had seen as a child. The static on her comm only unsettled her while she sat there. She slammed her fist onto the armrest and cursed. "One Bravo Six, this is One Bravo Recon. Requesting permission to enter the city."

The comm was silent for a long pause before the reply came through. "One Bravo Recon, you have permission, but damn it, Maeve, be careful in there."

Maeve smiled as she confirmed the order, then switched her comm to the lance channel. "Tomoko, lead us in, but go slow. We can't help anyone if we get ambushed. Saunders, Kelder, stay back at least a hundred meters, but not so far back you lose line of sight."

Before they even replied, she pushed her throttle bar forward and felt *Minerva* come to life. Smoke, and the growing darkness of the night made it hard to see without sensors. She switched her view to low light, and the buildings all lit up in green, a thin wireframe outlining them.

The *Raven* stepped around another burning tank as it rounded a corner. Maeve counted at least a dozen tanks and armored fighting vehicles so far, but she had yet to see any downed 'Mechs, friend or foe. Static squealed in her ear, and then a clear but gruff voice came over the channel.

"—Captain Donaldson, come around to the south and push those 'Mechs back." Major Mable Payne sounded firm and somehow still calm, even though Maeve could hear explosions in the background.

"Major, this is One Bravo Recon. We're moving in to assist, where do you need us?" Maeve said.

"You're not engaged yet, One Bravo Recon?" the surprised voice said. "All right, take your lance to thirty-four point twenty-three and secure that intersection. Watch the buildings as you go. There's infantry with portable heavy weapons all over the place." There was another explosion through the comm and a curse. "They are dropping buildings all over the city, trying to limit our mobility. We need to keep that intersection open, Lieutenant."

"Roger that, Major. We are headed there now." Maeve switched to her lance channel. "I'm sending new coordinates now. We need to get there quickly, but not so quickly that we're reckless. Command says there are infantry ambushers all over the place, so keep your eyes on your sensors."

The apprehension Maeve had felt before the mission now drifted away as she fell into her element. The smoke and the darkness made it hard to see what was off in the distant city. The *Raven* and its advanced sensors were only a couple of dozen meters ahead of the rest of the lance.

"Movement," Tomoko said, her 'Mech stopping abruptly. "It looks like civilians just trying to get somewhere safe."

"Let them go," Maeve said. "Once they have gotten clear, keep moving."

She advanced a few paces and saw a family scurrying across the road just ahead of Tomoko's bird-legged 'Mech. No sooner had the family left her HUD then she saw a flash, followed by two explosions that slammed into the side of the *Raven*, sending it crashing into a storefront on its left.

Maeve twisted to her left and raised *Minerva*'s arm, stitching a line of machine-gun fire along the building the attack came from. "Tomoko, status." She moved forward slowly, her arms up and ready in case there was another ambush.

The *Raven* shifted out of the rubble and struggled to its feet. "I'm good, Lieutenant. The missiles didn't do any real damage, but it looks like something got jarred loose in one of my medium lasers."

Maeve frowned. The last thing they needed was to worry about an ambush from every building they passed.

"Tomoko, I'll take the lead for a bit. Slide back into the Two position. Everyone else, close up the formation. No more than ten-meter intervals. Let's keep our eyes on the sensors and watch for heat signatures in all the buildings from here on out. But don't shoot unless you know for sure it's a hostile target."

They moved forward for another few minutes without problems, other than the smoke and the darkness. The intersection turned out to be a large roundabout with a fountain in the middle; several four-story buildings lined the streets on both sides.

"Spread out and secure the area," she ordered her lance. "Tomoko, take the north-forward approach, Kelder, you're on the right. Saunders, watch the rear. ECM on maximum."

Maeve stepped *Minerva* over to the road leading left, carefully avoiding several hovercars abandoned in the middle of the road. Checking the time and their location, she toggled her comm to the regimental channel. "Major, One Bravo Recon. We've secured the position."

"Sorry, One Bravo Recon, there were delays on our end. It looks like they've started to pull back farther into the city, and are fighting hard as they go. Continue moving north on that route. You should run into our lead elements."

Maeve checked her map again and added a waypoint to the screen.

"Be wary of ambushes, though," the major warned. "There are troops with portable rockets scattered through the city. The little bastards have caused a lot more trouble than we expected."

"We've encountered that already," Maeve replied. "Minimal damage so far, and no resistance other than that. We're moving now. One Bravo Recon out."

Throttling up her 'Mech, Maeve strode across the circular roads and found the street she was looking for. "All right, team, last leg before we meet the rest of the regiment. Tomoko, I'm taking point again."

The explosion caught the whole lance by surprise. The smoking crater in the road was just visible under the bulk of the *Raven* that was slumped over it. The 'Mech's right leg now ended in a stump where its clawed bird-like foot was supposed to be, and the beak-shaped nose had left a shallow divot in the grass next to the road.

"Everybody, freeze!" Maeve ordered. "Tomoko, report."

"My right foot is completely unresponsive. Actuators are locked up, and nothing below the knee is showing as active. I may be able to bypass something to get it moving."

Maeve frowned. The *Raven* was a casualty. Even if Tomoko could stand it back up, she couldn't move with what she had on hand. "Get out of there. There's nothing we can do at this point. Saunders, get up here and get Tomoko into your 'Mech. Kelder, move to the front and keep watch."

"Please, LT, give me a chance to figure something out," Tomoko pleaded. "I don't want to leave her."

"There's no time. Evac and get your ass moving. That's an order!"

Minutes crept by as Maeve watched the lone MechWarrior scramble up the chain ladder leading to the cockpit of Saunders' *Anubis*.

The *Wasp* shuffled a second as Kelder's voice came over the comm. "Lieutenant, we've got movement up here. It's a very big signature. Do you think it could be the—"

He never finished his sentence as three brilliant beams of man-made lightning speared his 'Mech, punching straight through its chest. The *Wasp* seized up and dropped to the street. Bits of gyro shot out of its back, and geysers of coolant jetted out.

"Contact! Saunders, get Tomoko inside *now*. We can't stand still any longer."

Maeve was already in motion even as she spoke. She raised *Minerva*'s right arm and stabbed pulses of energy into the darkness. She knew she needed to keep moving, but as the enemy 'Mech fully stepped out of the darkness, her urgency doubled. The 80-ton *Awesome* was nearly twice the mass of her own 'Mech, and packed enough firepower to engage her whole lance.

In the dark streets, she could almost see the glow of the capacitors as it loosed another trio of shots from its particle projection cannons. Spinning to the right, she managed to avoid two of them, but the third clipped her right forearm. Armor fractured and melted off the limb, exposing the vulnerable endo-steel skeleton underneath. Warning lights flashed on her console as her large laser turned red, and she cursed at losing half her firepower.

"We're closed up, Maeve," Saunders said, "Kelder is awake, but he's stuck in his 'Mech." Twenty missiles shot out from his shoulder-mounted launchers. More than half of the salvo impacted the *Awesome*, peppering it with explosions. Armor splintered and cracked in several places, but it was far from seriously damaged.

Saunders' attack had bought Maeve a few seconds, and she hoped to capitalize on the moment. She pushed down on her foot pedals and felt herself sink into the command couch as her jump jets rocketed the medium 'Mech high into the air. Maeve loved that *Minerva* could fly: it was as close to being a goddess as she could get.

Twisting in midair, she brought up her remaining medium laser and watched the beam slice a deep scar into the *Awesome*'s shoulder. She was rewarded with seeing the arm drop limply at its side, robbing the enemy 'Mech of a PPC.

As she was descending, two sets of missiles streaked out from the *Awesome* and slammed into her left leg. The force of the explosions sent her spinning out of control. The ground came up fast, but her left leg was out of position when she attempted to land. Her right leg hit the ground first, the myomer muscles flexing as it absorbed the landing. The left foot hit next and dragged along the concrete, causing *Minerva* to pitch forward. The torso and head hit the pavement hard, jerking her forward in her harness and dislocating her shoulder.

Alarms screamed at her as she looked down at the console. Red lights blinked angrily at her from multiple sources. Her shoulder ached as she scrolled through alerts, and a drop of blood splashed on the top of her hand. The damage readouts were showing red or not responding at all, and her heat was already redlining, which meant the fall must have punctured the engine shielding.

Time was as big an enemy as the *Awesome* stalking toward her. She tried as much as she could to get *Minerva* moving again, but the thundering vibrations of the approaching assault 'Mech made the final decision for her.

She fumbled with the straps holding her in place, and slammed into the cockpit canopy as soon as the harness let her go, blood from her head wound staining the glass. Crawling to the hatch, she slammed the emergency release and watched the hatch fly away as the explosive bolts did their job.

Pulling herself out of the cockpit, she glanced around and saw Kelder running away from his downed *Wasp*. The sight of the young MechWarrior made her smile. The kid had a bright future ahead of him, and she was glad he had at least survived his first battle.

A wave of intense heat washed over her as the *Awesome* fired its two remaining PPCs again, the heat of the attack forcing her back down into the cockpit. She felt as much as heard the massive 'Mech moving forward, advancing on the vulnerable *Anubis*.

Scrambling out of the cockpit, Maeve managed to get far enough away that she wasn't smashed underfoot when the massive enemy 'Mech stomped on *Minerva*'s head. She lay on the ground, eyes watching her legacy burn just a few meters away.

A hand on her shoulder jolted her back to the present. "Lieutenant, we need to get off the street right now!" Kelder yelled into her ear.

He pointed down the street where the *Awesome* had come from, and she could see several large shapes moving in the darkness. There was something familiar about them, but there wasn't time to sit around and wait for them to come closer. She and Kelder were exposed, and needed to get to cover.

The pain in her shoulder was intense, but Maeve pushed herself up to her feet. "We need to get behind a building, something solid."

He grabbed her by the arm and ran off the street just as the lead 'Mech came close enough to see them. The hum of magnetic energy filled the air as an *Orion* marched forward. She knew that 'Mech, it was one of First Battalion's.

The smile on her face faded quickly as the heavy 'Mech fired its Gauss rifle. The round moved so fast it was a flash across the night, but the impact on the *Awesome* was so loud that windows shattered around them, causing the most beautiful but deadly snowfall Maeve had ever seen.

Her ears rang, and she had to shout just to hear her herself, but she pushed Kelder toward a nearby alley. "Keep your head down and don't wander off. Retrieval will happen fast. And you did good today. I'll take you in my lance any time."

He crept forward slowly, and for the first time Maeve saw the small hold-out pistol in his hand, insurance against enemy ground troops. She smiled at that. He was well on his way to becoming a good soldier.

She pulled down a small flap on her cooling vest and pressed the button on her emergency transponder. It wouldn't allow her to communicate with anyone, but it would let friendly units know they were out here.

Maeve sat alone in the shadow of the DropShip, a bandage wrapped around her head. The medics had long since left her, focusing on other wounded. The regiment was almost loaded back onto the DropShips for travel back to Canopian space.

Footfalls caught her attention, and she saw Captain Dappel standing next to her. "The mission was a mess, but we got almost everyone back out alive, including all of your people. You did good, Maeve."

Maeve sighed and adjusted the sling on her arm. Her shoulder hadn't actually dislocated, but the injury from the fall would keep her riding a desk for the foreseeable future. "Good? I ran into another ambush and lost three-fourths of my lance, including my own *Phoenix Hawk*. I fail to see how I did good."

"You helped the regiment get out of an ugly spot, and you got your whole lance out alive," Dappel replied.

"Samantha, I lost my 'Mech—my *mother's* 'Mech—I'm Dispossessed now. Hell, almost my whole lance is Dispossessed." Maeve did not even look up.

"Lost, but not destroyed, Maeve. That means it's still out there, and those Hegemony bastards are likely going to repair it. You may think you won the battle only to lose the war, but there will be other raids. It's lost right now, but not gone forever." Captain Dappel placed a hand on Maeve's good shoulder and squeezed it gently.

Maeve turned her head and watched her CO walk away. *Lost right now, but not gone forever*—the line played over and over in her head. She knew Samantha was right, but she had lost the most important thing in her life. Not only was *Minerva* her BattleMech, it was a family heirloom.

"Lieutenant?"

The voice startled her, and she turned to see one of the ground troops standing about a meter away.

"Final loading procedures have started, so we'll be lifting off soon," the soldier said. "All nonessential personnel are to board now."

"Understood." Maeve looked in the direction of the city and nodded. "Don't get too comfortable, *Minerva*," she whispered. "I'll be back for you."

UNIT DIGEST:
OLD GUARD
(HANSEN'S ROUGHRIDERS)

BEN KLINEFELTER

Nickname: The Old Guard
Affiliation: Mercenary (Hansen's Roughriders)
CO: Major Ehric Reinhardt
Average Experience: Veteran/Fanatical
Force Composition: 1 Heavy Armor Company (Reinforced)
Unit Abilities: The Old Guard receives the Special Command Ability of Esprit De Corps and is not subject to Forced Withdrawal or Morale checks.
Parade Scheme: The Old Guard uses the standard Roughriders colors of tan and dun but with the addition of a small golden shield on every vehicle.

UNIT HISTORY

"I am the guardian in the darkness, the shield against the sword, the protector of those who cannot protect themselves, until my last breath leaves my body and my heart is stilled. I will fight with all my strength and wit so they may survive and live through the sacrifice I make." For close to 200 years, every initiate to the Old Guard has sworn this oath before the entire assembled unit, and any member found to break that oath is cast out in disgrace.

The Old Guard's origins began as an unofficial committee of retired MechWarriors, tankers, and infantry who volunteered to uphold some semblance of standards in the rough-and-tumble world of the Hansen's Roughriders mercenary unit. Working behind the scenes and outside of the chain of command, the Old Guard took care of small problems within the unit before they could become bigger problems, from acting as liaisons between the Roughriders' command and their dependents for various personal issues, to deciding on disciplinary issues that would cause issues, contractually or perceptually, for the regiment. They assisted the families of Roughriders who fell in combat through support, contributions, and time. Since the inception of the Old Guard, the line regulars of the Roughriders accepted their decisions and respected the group for all they did to protect the unit and its families.

During the Bromhead Massacre in 3067, the Old Guard fought and died to protect the unit's dependents when the Second Taurian Lancers attacked the Roughriders' settlement. The Old Guard saved a small group of dependents and hid them away, but at the cost of their own families. Bent on revenge, the Old Guard cobbled together a short company of tanks they had salvaged during the Second Lancers' attack and participated in the Pleiades campaign against the Taurian Concordat. The retired tankers trained former infantry and MechWarriors to be proficient gunners in the salvaged armor, and it paid dividends. During the campaign, the Old Guard racked up a surprising number of enemy kills, surpassing the Roughriders' regular tank units. Upon conclusion of the campaign, Colonel Wolfgang Hansen officially incorporated the Old Guard into the Roughriders as an all-volunteer armor company and spent a considerable amount to upgrade their equipment, bringing them in line with his vision of a heavy armor company that could be an anvil on which to break enemy forces.

The Old Guard played several pivotal roles during the Roughriders' assault on Terra to root out the Word of Blake. Colonel Hansen used their heavy and assault tanks to hammer the enemy and free up Roughrider 'Mech forces to flank the Blakists during several

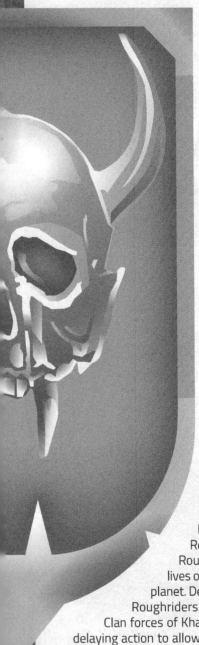

engagements. This culminated with the Old Guard destroying a Blakist Level III that attempted to ambush the mercenaries as they were escorting refugees. In Texas, the Word of Blake detonated several nuclear weapons to wipe out the regiment; the Roughriders, being no stranger to the effects of nuclear fire after their own war with the Concordat, weathered the storm, but at a steep cost, as the entire unit was nearly obliterated.

The quiet years following the foundation of the Republic of the Sphere saw the Old Guard assume a more protectant role for the Roughriders' dependents as the unit rebuilt itself into a stronger, tougher incarnation. The Old Guard held down the fort on Galatea while the Roughriders executed their contractual obligations off-planet. A raid by the rampaging Clan Jade Falcon saw the Old Guard step into the storm of fire once more. The company rumbled into action at Gilroy Crossing, stalling two Trinaries of Jade Falcons for several hours, destroying nine Falcon 'Mechs before the heavy armor was pushed out of the city. The Guard managed to tie up the Falcons long enough for Roughriders BattleMechs to reach the city and push the Falcons out, recovering lost ground and punishing the invaders for their temerity.

The Old Guard later accompanied the Roughriders to Terra on a contract to train the Republic Armed Forces. This contract found the Roughriders and the Old Guard fighting for their lives once again on Terra as Clan Wolf assaulted the planet. Deployed to Australia for training exercises, the Roughriders were the first to encounter the assaulting Clan forces of Khan Garner Kerensky. The Old Guard fought a delaying action to allow the Roughriders battalion to break contact from Clan Wolf forces, sacrificing themselves in the process. The Old Guard was overrun, the survivors taken prisoner. Their fate is currently unknown, but their sacrifices will be remembered by all the Roughriders who survived the battle for Terra.

COMPOSITION

The Old Guard is a reinforced heavy armor company within Hansen's Roughriders. Their primary organizational structure is three platoons of six tanks each. A fourth platoon of J-27 Ordnance Transports resupplies the unit while they are in heavy combat.

After the incorporation of the Old Guard into the Roughriders, the unit was grouped by types and chassis for organizational purposes. Prior to the RAF contract, Major Reinhardt reorganized the Old Guard to give each platoon a solid mix of firepower, utilizing his exclusive inventory of Challenger X MBTs, Bulwark assault tanks, DI Morgan assault tanks, and DI Schmitt tanks.

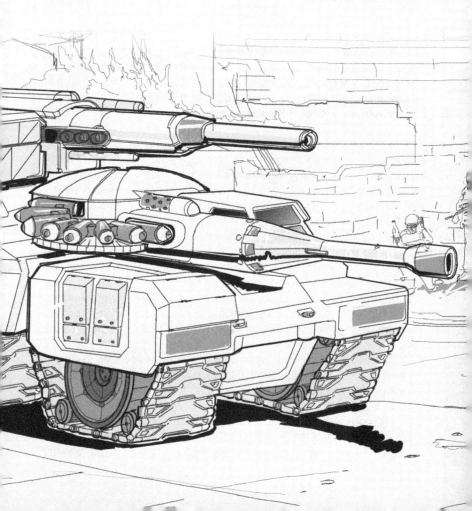

A FUNNY THING HAPPENED ON THE WAY TO THE HOMELAND

LORCAN NAGLE

Postscript to *Report on the Second Mutual Disarmament Policy Symposium, Terra, 3087*, by Professor Kieran McGrath, Political Science Department, Chekswa School of Literature, Donegal, Lyran Commonwealth. Originally published in the Winter 3087 issue of *Interplanetary Affairs* (Donegal University Press).

Following the end of the symposium, I had arranged to spend a little time on Terra to explore and investigate. After all, this is Terra, birthplace of humanity, and it might be my only opportunity to do so! I had been quite curious after seeing the disconnect between how representatives of the Republic of the Sphere from the Japanese Archipelago acted compared to the Draconis Combine delegation, and as I am a proud member of the Irish diaspora on Donegal, my first port of call had to be Letterkenny, the largest settlement in the Irish county that gave our world its name. And—well, I have to say it was quite a surprising trip. Shortly after arriving there, I discovered the most common pronunciation of the planet's name—*DAH-nuh-gull*—is not how the Irish on Terra pronounce the county name: *DUH-nee-gaul*, itself an anglicization of *Dún na nGall*, with the first word pronounced like *dune*, and the last pronounced like *nawl*.

My time there became a far more interesting experience. I almost played anthropologist as I compared how we do things in Media City as opposed to Letterkenny, and indeed other towns and cities in Ireland. There is a rivalry between the people of Donegal and of Arc-Royal over who is more authentically Irish, and it appears the answer is "Neither." For example, it's often argued whether the traditional meal families prepare for holidays and special occasions is corned beef and cabbage (on Arc-Royal), or pork and cabbage (on Donegal), but neither is eaten in Ireland.

I visited Dublin and sat down with Professor Orlaith Marchlewski, an anthropologist from Trinity College who specializes in comparisons between traditional Terran cultures and their descendants in the Inner Sphere. Apparently, it's an entire school of thought on Terra which we've had very little exposure to, thanks to ComStar's, and later Word of Blake's insular control of the planet. Orlaith told me that bacon and cabbage was a staple in Ireland, but over a thousand years ago, when the island was a territory of neighboring Britain, and the indigenous population was very poor. The meal fell aside in favor of more lavish dishes following their independence and development as a nation-state. However, the tradition prospered in an earlier Irish diaspora—one that saw enclaves of Irish people settle primarily in North America and Australasia in the nineteenth century, and in Professor Orlaith's opinion, it's likely that many traditions both of our worlds see as authentically Irish come from North Americans who emigrated outward while still claiming Irish heritage.

As I left Ireland behind, I found similar cultural discontinuities on my travels. For example, I have always enjoyed the stories centered around hillside bandits with hearts of gold, which are a longstanding part of media produced on the Federated Suns world of Andalusia. While there was a tradition of such stories in the region of Spain that Andalusia takes its name from, that has long faded into the realm of tacky tourism on Terra.

For a more recent phenomenon, I learned that officers in the Duchy of Oriente's military have taken to wearing an empty scabbard as part of their dress uniform. They claim it's in homage to Force Commander Christian Maldonado, a twenty-sixth-century infantry officer from the Fusiliers of Oriente. According to the story, he was killed during the Reunification War when he handed a Canopian his sword as a gesture of good faith, and was promptly ran through with his own blade. However, Maldonado was actually shot dead. It seems there's a connection back to an old Spanish tradition which claims it's bad luck to give knives as a gift unless one receives a coin in exchange, and over the centuries, this has become linked to Maldonado's death as a piece of latter-day folklore.

Despite these differences, and the frequent sense of bemusement from the people I spoke with about the way some people of the Inner Sphere hearken back to their Terran heritage, there was very little resentment about it. I think a lot of that is because in my case, I'm a Lyran first. I speak German and English, and didn't present myself as somehow being Terran or even Irish while I was there. Professor Marchewski explained that during early cultural diasporas on Terra, cultural enclaves that formed often claimed a more direct connection back to their source region, and ignored the drift that began pretty much immediately in a timeframe where communication between Terra's continents was slow and travel between them was expensive and relatively rare. When those conditions changed, the cultural shifts were already well-established.

The scales involved in the Inner Sphere are even greater than those on Terra before the development of global telecommunications and cheap intercontinental flight. In the nineteenth century, it took around a week to cross the Atlantic Ocean, whereas today it takes that long to transit from a jump point to most inhabited systems, to say nothing of waiting at jump points as your JumpShip charges or you transfer from one JumpShip to another. The vast majority of people will never leave the continent where they were born, and of those who do, most won't leave their homeworld, and an even smaller number will venture outside the borders of the interstellar nation they live in, let alone visit Terra and encounter the culture that informed their homeworld's. When it does happen, migration is more likely to be between worlds within a nation, so even in cases where a single ethnic or cultural group initially colonized a world, their culture will mingle with their neighbors and begin to take on more and more elements of the broader national identity. Even with the relative speed of hyperpulse-generator communications, a world's ties back to Terra or another world of origin fade over time, and firsthand access to the source culture declines or vanishes completely.

With that in mind, as my time on Terra ended, I decided to offer an invitation to Professor Marchewski to come to Donegal and see what post-diaspora culture is like, to return the gracious favor she provided me. Thanks to the new Terran regime, she and her colleagues are free to travel across the entire Inner Sphere, and they are all very excited to gain firsthand experience of the culture they've only experienced both at a distance and through ComStar and Word of Blake's ideological filters over the last three centuries. And I, for one, am excited to be one of the first to show it to them.

DYING BREED

GEOFF "DOC" SWIFT

SPACEPORT GAMMA
HELLREACH MOUNTAINS
GALICIA
SCORPION EMPIRE
14 MARCH 3099

Lishi shrugged against the bluster of Galicia's arctic winter, the wind tickling the traces of her neural implants. She kept her fists clenched in her parka's pockets so no one could see the tremors and twitching fingers. Willpower alone had not kept the signs of her degeneration at bay for some time, and now even medication could no longer compensate.

Her liberty to the Galician arctic had failed to rejuvenate her. Not even the sight of introduced ice hellion packs could stave off the combination of age and neural degradation, though their movements brought joy nonetheless. Watching a pack drag down a sure-hoofed cliff mammoth bull had been nothing short of magnificent, but the joy was short lived. The ordered period of rest and relaxation was over.

A roar from above barely caught her notice. The asymmetrical whine of the *Lion*-class *Steel for Gold* was quite familiar. Ancient damage to the engine bell had been long since repaired, but the mismatched old and new materials vibrated at different frequencies. After hearing it scores of times, it was easy to identify at even more than a kilometer away.

She turned from the vista and trod along the plowed path cut through hip-deep snow. Her steps were short and measured, both to avoid slipping on the slick ferrocrete and to limit any spasms that might afflict her limbs. Her hands stayed in her pockets, eschewing the handrail out of pride. The others waiting for transport off Galicia might see, and Lishi could not bear it if whispers arose. She slowed her pace and allowed the others to pass by.

They all moved with precision, fitting the charges of a Seeker. As they left her behind, she relaxed slightly. It was difficult at the best of times, and it had been many months since anything approaching the best of times. Fingers that terminated far too close to her shoulders, toes that should stretch well past her 1.5-meter height, eyes that should be able to note the slightest movement of enemies at distances well beyond 500 meters, and senses that far outstripped those of normal humans should be at her constant command. But she had been apart from the rest of her body for the last three months. As the *Steel for Gold* settled onto Landing Pad 4, carrying the best part of her in its hold, the distance was still too great. Reunion would be appreciated, but also reluctant. Every disconnection was harder than the last. One day, severing the connection might come at the cost of her life.

Personnel disembarked from the *Lion*, most from the cavernous bay doors. Some used the narrow gangway that gently extended from the quarters section. She headed for the latter, wishing to speak to Seeker Nearchos. Lishi nodded to the rest of his retinue, those who had not wintered on Galicia. None met her eyes. It was not a new experience. Few people enjoyed meeting her gaze, bloodshot eyes rarely able to focus on any point for more than a microsecond, occasionally lit from within by a misfiring neural trace.

But this was different. Even the other yeomen looked away rather than greet her as a fellow warrior in the service of Nearchos. Her heart raced, pulse pounding in her ears like the pealing of the Great Bell of the Cathedral of Saint James in Pilgrim's Square, at the center of Ferrol, Galicia's capital city.

Her boot soles touched the metal gangway, and she quickened her pace. Charges stepped aside rather than be shouldered out of the way. The threshold of the DropShip forced her to pause and allow her brutalized eyes to adjust to the darkness of the interior after the bright white of the mountainside.

"Star Captain."

Lishi straightened. No one had called her that in years.

Blinking rapidly, she turned. Seeker Nearchos, tall and proud MechWarrior that he was, cut a fine figure. His blue uniform was immaculate, matching daggers at his hips, with the heraldry of the Scorpion Empire on the right shoulder and a smaller ensign of the former Clan Ice Hellion on his left. He was the most prominent of the few former Hellion warriors amongst the Seekers.

Lishi, like the rest of his charges, had also been a warrior of that Clan. But she had been addressed as "Yeoman Lishi" since he claimed her as a bondsman. Not since the warriors of her Star had been killed fighting Hansa-sponsored privateers had she been called a Star Captain.

An involuntary shudder ran down her spine, accompanied by spasms in her hands and feet. She had been pulled from the wreckage of her *Minotaur* that day, wishing she had died within it. Worse than the loss of her subordinates, *all of them*, at the hands of *stravag* pirates had been the loss of her ProtoMech. It had truly been a part of her, and she had never felt whole since.

"Lishi..." Nearchos' compassion-filled voice trailed off, and he nodded toward his quarters. "Come."

The room was spartan, typical for the average Clan warrior but less so for Seekers, whose ostentation was well-known. Instead of ancient tchotchkes and rare artifacts lining walls and shelves, his room bore only a sleeping mat and a bare table that served as a desk and dining surface. He sat in the one chair and placed his palms on the desk. "Lishi, your time in my retinue is over."

"Sir, may I ask how I have failed you?" She held her hands behind her back, clasping them together in a vain effort to still the sudden onslaught of tremors.

"You have not. Not once. Ever. But your *Delphyne* took severe damage from the Diamond Sharks on Wark." Nearchos swallowed and looked at the table. "The parts used to repair it were the last we had. There are none left to be had in the Imperio."

Lishi winced. It was the Castilians who insisted on calling their nation the Imperio. Most of the Clan properly called it the Scorpion Empire, but some had taken to using the local appellation. She was not one of them. "And the last three months?"

"*Neg*, my quest failed. I could not locate any spares. Your kind has become less and less present on the battlefield. With the Khan deeming ProtoMechs wasteful three years ago, no new ProtoMechs are being built, no replacement parts being manufactured. The need for another specialized version of weapons and equipment..." Nearchos trailed off.

He need not say more. Lishi had heard it all many times before. When her Star was lost, only a handful of ProtoMech Points remained in the Empire. Had not Nearchos taken her in a Trial of Possession because of their shared Ice Hellion ancestry, she might have been assigned to a *solahma* Cluster as worthless foot infantry. Likewise, he had acquired a *Delphyne* and all the spare parts he could find. Lishi had not asked about the ProtoMech's former pilot. No new ProtoMech pilots were entering the warrior caste, not with the high resource cost for training and implant surgery, especially for a "wasteful" combat unit. Those who washed out of training were too useful in the other castes of the newborn Empire.

Nearchos spoke again.

Lishi shook her head, arresting the drift she had succumbed to. She had not heard his words. "Say again, sir?"

"Lishi, you are the last ProtoMech pilot in the Imperio."

"What *solahma* Cluster am I being transferred to, sir?" Lishi whispered the words, keeping the huskiness of emotion from her voice.

Nearchos stared at her in silence for nearly a full minute. "The Three-Fourteenth Planetary Garrison Cluster on Graystone took losses in a Hansa raid six weeks ago. I will deliver you there."

"Yes, sir." Angry thoughts swam disjointedly through her head. Perhaps she could declare a Trial of Grievance to stay in his retinue, or to obtain a better posting. But what use is one ProtoMech to a combat unit? She knew the answer. To a Seeker, whose retinue might benefit from an eclectic assembly of disparate elements, a lone ProtoMech might make sense. A front-line commander would have no use for her. A quick death would be her only true goal in such a trial, and she was not eager for death. Yet.

Resigned, she said, "I may be dismissed, *quiaff*?"

"*Aff*, Star Captain," Nearchos said with a nod.

Lishi turned smartly on her heel and stepped out of the Seeker's quarters, closing the hatch behind her. She fought down her emotions for a moment and executed another parade-perfect turn. Her footsteps were steady and fast. She opened the hatch to her quarters and sidestepped in, closing it quietly behind her.

She pulled her bunk from the wall and sat on the edge of it. In a moment she was up and pacing. Then sitting, rocking forward and back and pounding her fists into her thighs. Pacing again. Leaning back against the bulkhead, staring at the ceiling, trying futilely to still her hands, control her roaming eyes. Pacing. Sitting restlessly. Standing, clutching her left biceps with her right hand, rubbing up and down, trying to figure out what to do with her left hand. Sitting, tapping one foot and bouncing the other leg with her toes as the pivot, unable to still the twitching of her fingers and cursing herself. She grabbed the tiny foam square that served as a pillow and crushed it to her face, roaring in anger and self-hatred and helplessness.

Finally, the tears came. Crying hurt. Not emotionally, physically. The implanted interface traces activated sporadically to the salt in her tears, which acted as an electrolyte. Shocks ran through her eyeballs and lids, and all throughout her face. The old circuitry could not even allow her to experience human emotions anymore. Pain might have galvanized her once, but now it merely reminded her of the depths she had fallen to...from which only one route offered escape.

GARRISON POST IOTA
WITCHCLAW RAVINE
GRAYSTONE
SCORPION EMPIRE
3 JULY 3099

Star Captain Lishi looked out at the faces of Trinary Sigma Two. Some were pinched and red, others slack and sallow. She recognized them all as expressions she had worn since being condemned to *solahma* status.

She dismissed her subordinates. They turned listlessly and shuffled out of the hangar. Once she might have railed at them for moving at anything less than a run, for anything short of fervent pursuit of their duties. Some had been MechWarriors. Some had led Elemental Stars. Others had crewed tanks or aerofighters. Only she had been a ProtoMech pilot. But they were all the same now.

Useless. Cannon fodder. Hoping to die in battle.

Lishi lingered in the hangar, realizing her thought was not exactly accurate. A few quick strides took her to the rear of the cheap sheet-metal structure, where the wan light of dawn could not dispel the shadows from the farthest corner.

Slumped against the wall, behind stacked barrels of lubricant and crates of long-storage rations was her *Delphyne*. The other condemned had arrived with only their uniforms, the trappings of their former postings left behind. BattleMechs and tanks and battlesuits were too valuable to remain in the hands of the old and useless. But there were no other ProtoMech pilots to succeed her in the cockpit of her *Delphyne*, so it had been left behind with her. One more piece of obsolete war equipment, useless to Clan Goliath Scorpion.

Her wristchron beeped, and a touch silenced it. She stared for a few more moments. The twitching of her fingers had amplified, and her hands and forearms moved spasmodically without her notice. She sighed, turned on a heel, and marched to the Star Colonel's office.

The Star Colonel and the other Trinary commanders were waiting when she arrived. She slipped into the office and sidled laterally from the doorway. Star Colonel Rossiton flicked a glare her way, but said nothing.

Fifteen minutes later, the same orders as the day before and the day before and the day before were reissued. Each Trinary patrolled on the same route around the settlement's construction site, on the same schedule. The daily briefings reminded them all of being real warriors, accepting real orders with legitimate objectives, bidding for the honor to take a particular prize... But those days were gone. *Solahma* warriors longed for their final battle, any battle, to end the waiting, the monotony, the dread of uncertainty. It was an unfamiliar emotion for Clan warriors. Better for it to end quickly, lest it become familiar. The possibility of such familiarity was truly terrifying, and no warrior could live long with that.

Rossiton wrapped up his orders. "Dismissed. Star Captain Lishi, remain."

Lishi stiffened and clenched her fists behind her back. The others filed out. None looked her way.

"Close the door." Rossiton sank into the chair behind his desk.

She closed the door and came to attention. Her hands wavered at her sides despite her efforts to still them.

Rossiton rubbed a hand over his face. His face was pale, his pate bare. Only his brown eyes and a millimeter of steel-gray stubble wrapping the back of his head gave him any color. Crow's-feet radiated from his eyes, and other wrinkles creased his chin and forehead. He was decades older than she, and looked as miserable as a warrior might imagine.

"I expect my officers to appear on time for my briefings, Star Captain."

"*Aff*, Star Colonel."

Sighs were issued on the base far more often than orders, and the Star Colonel voiced one for the ages. He rose and looked out the window toward the dust cloud rising from the excavators digging out earth for the massive ferrocrete pad of a future spaceport. "This is not the end I anticipated." He looked over his shoulder at her. "Nor you, I believe." He turned back to the window. "No end for a warrior. Survive all your battles, winning all save your Trial of Bloodright, and this is your reward. Would that I had died in Operation Ice Storm." He mumbled something subaudible and trailed off.

Several minutes passed when he was motionless as a statue, watching the dust rise into the air.

Finally he turned back to her. "Would that we both died then, *quiaff?*"

Lishi clenched her jaw, remembering the hell the Jade Falcons had brought to bear on them. The sting of defeat. She had not been with then-saKhan Connor Rood like the Star Colonel. Her Point had barely escaped. Then the long journey back toward the Homeworlds, only to be absorbed by the Scorpions. That was better than annihilation. Or was it? Hunting down her lost comrades, bringing some into the new fold, being forced to slay those who would not submit. Those were memories she wished she had never made.

She met Rossiton's gaze, and he did not look away. A look of understanding passed between them. Together, they nodded.

"We are a dying breed, Star Captain. Few of Clan Ice Hellion remain, including our Khan. His efforts to preserve our ways in Beta Galaxy can only go so far. Soon it will fall to those of Scorpion ancestry to keep the traditions alive, but will they bother? I doubt it."

"I share your doubts, Star Colonel, but what does it matter? We shall be dead long before our expectations come to pass."

"I wish I shared your optimism, Star Captain." He turned back to the window. His bearing and posture remained formal and proper, but he seemed to shrink in Lishi's eyes.

After a few minutes of silence, even without being dismissed, she opened the door and left.

SETTLEMENT BAKER
PATROL ROUTE FOUR
GRAYSTONE
SCORPION EMPIRE
22 OCTOBER 3099

Months of interminable monotony were broken only by the rapid progress of the spaceport. The new colony would need supplies by the shipload, which meant a place to land those ships to unload their cargo. Already four immense landing pads were complete, with four more still under construction. Habitation stacks were being assembled from prefabricated blocks, so the personnel to operate the spaceport could be close to hand when needed. Additional settlements were being constructed equidistant from the spaceport in locations the scientist caste had identified as ideal.

Trinary Sigma Two rounded the bend of Settlement Baker. Their unarmed patrol vehicles held a loose formation on the dirt track the laborer caste's excavators had created between Baker's new reservoir and the village proper.

A voice crackled over the comms. Lishi, in the passenger seat of the lead vehicle, fumbled awkwardly with the comm, silently cursing her uncooperative fingers. She managed to turn up the volume and adjust the channel to clear up the audio. Pulling the handset close to her mouth, she pressed the talk bar. "Sigma Two actual here. Say again."

"Base under attack. Return to base. Hostiles are—" A burst of static erupted from the speakers.

"Sigma Two to base. Say again, base, say again."

There was no response.

She met her driver's gaze. Ansel had driven a hovertank before being replaced by younger warriors. Neither said a word. Ansel looked back to the dirt road and pressed the accelerator pedal to the floor. Lishi's head smacked into the headrest at the sudden speed. The internal combustion engine roared like a wounded beast. Ansel did not slow for bends in the road, slewing through turns in great sprays of dirt and loose stone. His eyes were fixed ahead, unblinking. His face was set like stone, but it wore a smile. He was back in his element, speeding recklessly and maneuvering as only a hoverjock could.

The safety restraints bit hard into her with every spin of the steering wheel. The g-forces reminded her of her own piloting, made her feel at home. She swung her head around, saw the rest of the patrol hot on their rear.

Iota Base came into view, and Lishi gasped. The ovoid shape of a DropShip rested on one of the new landing pads. The distinct shape of BattleMechs lurked in the greasy black smoke rising from the flames consuming the new hab stacks.

The only BattleMech in the 314th was Star Colonel Rossiton's ancient *Flashman*. He had won a Trial of Possession to retain it after being reassigned to the Cluster. But she could not make out the specific 'Mechs through the smoke. Part of her hoped Rossiton was still alive and fighting, but the rest of her hoped he had already been killed, that his days as a *solahma* commander were over.

Ansel slewed the patrol car to a stop, and Lishi was bounding over the closed passenger door before it came to rest. She sprinted for the hangar, Ansel close behind her. The other cars arrived seconds later. One erupted into a fireball. An oppressive wave of heat washed over her. She had not seen the laser, but it had to be a large one. She did not mourn her dead comrades. Such was the *solahma* way.

They entered the hangar. It had not been flattened yet, so the attackers must not have thought much of the ramshackle building. Lishi thanked them for that. Ansel broke to the left, heading for the infantry arsenal. He slung a pair of rocket launchers over his shoulder and grabbed a pair of satchel charges while sprinting back out the bay door. Others entered as Lishi ran for the far corner.

A crate held her cooling suit. She stripped and pulled it on in a flash. She shoved the crate toward the *Delphyne*, heaving a second crate atop it. She climbed up the unsteady assembly and into the open chest of the ProtoMech. Before the hatch closed, she powered up.

She gasped as a shudder ran down her spine and along her limbs. It continued past her fingertips, finally reconnecting her to the parts she had missed for so many months. Her breath came short and sharp. Welcome tingling ran up and down her as she stretched out her true limbs and senses, taking in the world with greater clarity and perfection than her biological organs could ever provide. She closed her eyes and rocked in the comforting grip of her *Delphyne*, twitching no longer in the agony of amputation, but in the ecstasy of being made whole.

Her head lolled as she tensed and relaxed in rapid succession, smiling for the first time in months. Her breathing steadied and her eyes opened again. For a moment, she forgot where she was, a sheen of sweat now between her skin and the cooling suit.

Recollection of the situation hit her like an *Atlas'* fist. She pushed off the hangar wall and found her footing. MechWarriors and fighter pilots connected to their machines through their neurohelmets, but that was nothing compared to the direct neural link that allowed her to control her *Delphyne*. She *was* her ProtoMech, and it was her. They were one being, finally complete after too long apart. Her movements were its movements.

She sprinted for the hangar door, scattering barrels and crates in her wake. Sensors painted enemy units in red, a dozen of them. A thirteenth return showed as green. Rossiton's *Flashman*. He was across the vast platform composed of the landing-pad array, taking shots from three enemy BattleMechs and returning fire at a prodigious rate. Her sensors painted him green as friendly, but the heat building up in his 'Mech made him glow red in her view.

One of the enemies dropped, but Rossiton stumbled. Seven red symbols glowed between Lishi and her commander. One of those rocked as a group of infantry fired rockets at it. Cooling bodies on the ferrocrete proved the futility of untrained troops trying to mount anti-'Mech attacks.

Lishi locked her targeting reticle on the enemy 'Mech, a *Wasp*, and spat a coherent beam of light from her reptilian mouth. It struck the 20-ton 'Mech in the torso. Its thin armor, already pitted by rocket warheads, split like an overripe fruit. Her beam caught the *Wasp*'s missile ammunition, and the explosion turned the 'Mech into a dead husk. The contrails of an ejection seat rose above the carcass that teetered on its feet before collapsing to the ferrocrete.

Another explosion sounded from the distance. One of the red telltales engaged with the Star Colonel had vanished, but so too had his green icon.

Return fire cut through the smoke toward her. A coruscating blue beam grazed her left arm, and Lishi shrieked in pain. Her movements were the *Delphyne*'s, but its pain was her pain. Panting at the exertion and agony, she jumped. Arcing 150 meters through the air, she rose above the smoke, allowing her to see some of the enemy units clearly for the first time. They were all light and medium 'Mechs of obsolete design. They all bore the same ensign, a sailing vessel on a disc with the numeral 5: Regional Defense Force Five of the Hanseatic League. The Hansa had attacked the Empire's other colony worlds, trying to stop the Clan's expansion. It was her duty to stop them.

Some of the BattleMechs were engaging the other *solahma* Trinaries. The infantry was faring poorly, and few of them remained.

As the only true threat to the Hansa, most of the enemies focused their attention on her.

Lishi smiled. This was her time. This was what she had longed for these months on Graystone: a pitched battle against insurmountable odds. Only in such a fight might she prove her worth as a warrior, but also be guaranteed the combat death she craved.

A game of ice hellion and pack moose developed as she used the obscuring smoke and her maneuverability to stay ahead of the enemy guns. Alternating between sprints and jumps, constantly changing direction and target, she wove a web of deception and fury. A *Stinger* fell, its gyro melted to scrap as she blasted away its back armor. A second *Wasp* lost a leg.

A laser carved into her from the side, taking her arm off at the shoulder. She stumbled and went to one knee as a follow-up strike passed over her head. She silenced her screams at the traumatic amputation, got her feet back under her, and took off once again.

A *Wolverine* cut her off, its autocannon blasting and lasers blazing. She kicked off and soared over its head, turning a 180 and landing behind it. She blasted its back and took off again before it could turn.

The enemies were closing in, forming a ring to bottle her up, so Lishi spun on her heel and fired, a pirouette of savage warfare. Her foes rocked under the assault.

Something punched her to the ground. She stared at the sky, fighting for breath. Her limbs flailed, not responding to her commands. Her mouth tasted of metal. A viscous fluid ran down her belly. Her feet were cold. The breath of a breeze kissed flesh newly exposed to the air.

A large shape moved into view, blocking the sky. The large, misshapen shoulder was unmistakable: the boxy housing of a *Hunchback*'s massive Class-20 autocannon. It leaned in, looking her over. Almost calmly, it stepped around toward the feet she could no longer feel. The reverberations of its steps jolted her spine and awakened a new pain.

Her abdomen burned like nothing she had ever felt before. Her arms grew cold to match the legs that now seemed absent. Her vision blurred. The sensory inputs from the *Delphyne* wavered, sending static into her neural traces and making sure she felt every last iota of pain her body could still register.

The *Hunchback* leaned further, lining up its cannon for the death blow. It did not fire. Instead it turned. The contrails of small rockets arced toward it. The 'Mech twisted its torso to the side and fired a punishing salvo of ordnance.

When it turned back, smoke rose from the maw of its autocannon. Again it leaned forward. Sound issued from its external speakers. "Don't know what the hell you are, Clanner, but soon that won't matter."

She tongued her own external speakers, not certain they still functioned. "I am a dying breed, Hansa *stravag*. And so are you."

Her targeting reticle settled onto the enemy 'Mech's cockpit. She spat fire at the same time its cannon roared at her, a simultaneous exchange of murderous fury.

And her pain vanished.

MERCENARY ENTERTAINMENT NETWORK DIGEST: DECEMBER 3151

KEN' HORNER

The life of a mercenary can make staying current on your latest holovid shows difficult, with constant travel often in foreign realms. The Mercenary Entertainment Network will keep you up to date on the latest happenings of your favorites, and hopefully introduce you to new programs as well.

THE STEINHEARTS

A fictional docudrama loosely based on House Steiner, this holovid series has stood the test of time and is once again at the top of the ratings and award lists.

The Latest

Having rescued his sister from pirates, Rudinger Steinheart discovers Alexandria is pregnant, and suspects her kidnapping wasn't actually against her will at all. Meanwhile, the Fourth Royal Brigade has started a minor offensive against Clan Hawk while Rudinger's Uncle Rudolph leaves on a diplomatic mission to Tamar, though perhaps he doesn't have the same goals as Rudinger. On Skye, Octavia Kelso-Steinheart secretly negotiates with the mercenary Coyote's Grenadiers to provide two regiments to support an uprising against the Clan occupation, but someone in the resistance is reporting to the Clan Watch!

DAOSHEN LIAO: JUNIOR-HIGH CHANCELLOR

This Republic comedy finds Daoshen Liao as the head of Sian Junior High. Only he is aware of his true nature, and everyone else laughs off his claims of being the Chancellor of the Capellan Confederation. The signature line is his cry "But I'm the Celestial Wisdom!" and the reply, from any actor on the show, "For this school, yes sir!"

The Latest

Superintendent Lee needs to shut down a school in his district and has his sights set on Sian Junior High. Daoshen not only needs to keep his school open, but also deal with a strike by the servitors and the Caruso twins switching identities and driving their teachers crazy.

CONSPHERICY

Produced on Taurus IV, this show investigates conspiracy theories from across the Inner Sphere, with a slight bias toward Federated Suns- and Taurian Concordat-focused theories.

The Latest

The "Davion Shift": Why has the Federated Suns suffered huge losses to both the Capellan Confederation and the Draconis Combine? There are a lot of theories, but the latest points at a shift of forces to their Periphery borders, as if there was or is an invasion planned.

The First Wolf Empire: The return of the Clans eventually led to the creating of the Wolf Empire, but what about the failed attempts prior to the Jihad, when Wolf's Dragoons attempted to create their own little sphere of influence? Could the root of the Jihad be traced to the Dragoons' shenanigans and attacks on Blakist systems? Why hasn't this been more thoroughly examined?

TAMAR KNIGHTS

This animated show follows a group of teenage Knights of Tamar fighting to free Tamar worlds from their occupiers, with each episode offering a life lesson.

The Latest

The Knights travel into the Rasalhague Dominion to help a small community of fishermen throw off the chains of Clan oppression. Once there, they attempt to help the people build a resistance force, but find their interactions very odd, aside from the village outcast. The Knights are about to attend a festival when the outcast warns them that the festival is a trap! It turns out the community is a group of Dominion loyalists hoping to capture the Knights and deliver them to the Clan leaders. The Knights barely escape the ambush, and have to fight their way off planet, taking their new friend with them. They learn an important lesson about being nice to people and how that pays off in the end.

FALCON'S JUSTICE

The most-watched show in Clan-occupied space follows the investigation and then prosecution of major criminal violations. Unlike similar shows from the past, this is a reality show, and does not concern itself with redacting the identities of those involved.

The Latest

The inquisitors investigate a group of smugglers providing luxury goods to lower-caste members. The episode takes a dramatic turn when the inquisitors discover an artisan has been reselling these goods to bankroll a group of rebels. The artisan looks to be facing execution when a member of the Clan Watch steps in and adds a dramatic twist to the case.

YOU WRECK IT, WE 'MECH IT

Unfortunate or unskilled MechWarriors get a surprise from the Harding Repair Squad, who will not only rebuild the damaged 'Mech, but will upgrade it to a state-of-the-art war machine. The MechWarrior is kept mostly in the dark until the end, though after a couple of upgrades that diverge from the strengths of the pilot, the team generally will go over the general path of the rebuild.

The Latest

The Squad tackles an ancient *Charger* that shows all the hallmarks of being used as its name suggests. The speed is dramatically boosted with a new engine, Myomer Accelerator Signal Circuitry system, and supercharger. Some new armor and some small upgrades to the weaponry turns this lowly regarded brawler into a feared collision demon.

SHIPS OF THE SLDF

This show started as a local program in Regulus, and has blossomed into a show popular across the Inner Sphere and one that rarely faces censorship in any realm. Each week the show focuses on a Star League Defense Force WarShip, examining the capabilities and history of the ship. The conclusion of each episode puts the WarShip into a few simulated battles (or in rare instances, actual battle footage).

The Latest

The storied history of the SLS *Fred T. Berry*, a *Lola III* that saw action in freeing Terra from Amaris' control and left in the Exodus. Named after a captain of one of the first military airships who died with the loss of his craft, the *Fred T. Barry* was laid down in 2694 and was a lone wolf in the Periphery for decades until the Amaris Civil War saw the WarShip return to fleet action. After intense fighting around Mars, the ship joined General Kerensky's Exodus and eventually found new life as the *Storm Cat* in the Clan Smoke Jaguar fleet.

SEA*LIST ADS:
THE KANDERSTEG CATALOG

STEPHEN TOROPOV

[Distributed via transmission and hardcopy on Kandersteg, Lyran Commonwealth, January 3152]

PUBLIC NOTICE
8 January 3152
City of Thun, Bali, Kandersteg

GOODS AND SERVICES

Deploy in Style with Pixelgloss!

Need to get your company in parade trim before you ship out? Try Malirovka Corporation's new **Pixelgloss Armor Enamel**, available in 27 color varieties. Our proprietary formula is scratch-resistant, stain-resistant, and colorfast under prolonged exposure to the stellar spectrum of 87% of inhabited systems. It applies easily to all brands of standard and ferro-fibrous armor plating*, and common contaminants rinse right off. Minimize the time your valuable equipment spends in the paint shed with Pixelgloss Armor Enamel.

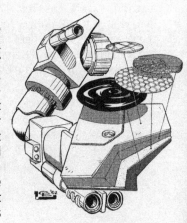

*Results not guaranteed with reflective, ferro-lamellor, and most reinforced armor compounds.

Grand Opening

Prepare for explosive savings! To celebrate the opening of the new Arcturan Arms Outlet, we've slashed prices at merchant outlets across the whole Kandersteg Arms Emporium complex. Save up to 5% on Mauser and Gray small arms and ammunition, take advantage of low-interest financing on BattleMechs from Kaiser Systems and TharHes Industries, and browse the new stock of Arcturan Arms Longarm-brand autocannons and specialty ammo! Delivery contracts are available for the mercenary on the move! Don't wait, these savings are for a limited time only! Mention this advertisement at the Emporium entrance to receive a 2-for-1 meal-deal coupon, redeemable at the TacoShark franchise in the food court.

PUBLIC INTEREST

Zoning Regulation Ballot Question: Private Military Industries

Per requirement of the Thun City Charter and in the interest of promoting informed voters, below are arguments for and against the proposed alteration to local zoning regulations, which would enlarge the city's designated zones for military-equipment storage. This issue will be on the ballot in the next civic election.

> "The proposed alteration to our zoning regulations is in the best economic interest of Thun as a city. Currently, the zoning board is overwhelmed by requests for variances to allow new accommodations for the mercenary market. The economic activity generated by the booming business of the hiring hall is of benefit to the whole city, and our regulations should not stand in the way of developers seeking to support that trade."
>
> —RAFIQ VON CARENTAN,
> REPRESENTING CITIZENS FOR A THRIVING THUN

> "Zoning regulations exist to keep the residents of a city safe. Relaxing the regulations that limit the storage of military materiel, including live ammunition, within city limits would actively make the streets of Thun less safe. While the hiring hall is bringing business to Thun and all of Kandersteg, this market is historically subject to drastic booms and busts, and we should not permanently alter the landscape of our city to accommodate an ephemeral industry."
>
> —TAQIYYA BINTI AATIF,
> REPRESENTING THE COMMUNITY SAFETY ORGANIZATION OF KANDERSTEG

PERSONAL MESSAGES

Message to E:
> Yes, to the stars and back. —Freelancer

ARTS AND CULTURE

Symphonic Season Begins

The Kandersteg Classical Azurewave Orchestra cordially invites the public to their new season of performances at the Thun Odeon Theater. This season will feature compositions by both the renowned symphonist Gertrude binti Lokiha and azurewave iconoclast Mazeed bin Izzat, and the premiere of Donegal-born composer Charley McCabe's first foray into Kanderstegian musical forms. Reserve your tickets through the KCAO's infonet box office today! Veterans of the Lyran Commonwealth Armed Forces and credentialed members of the Lyran Free Traders Association are eligible for discounted ticket prices.

Carvings Unveiled

The Budiaman Memorial Institute of Art is pleased to present an exhibition of carvings rendered in rare Alyina Cloud Forest hardwoods. Celebrating these sublime materials that have been unavailable to Lyran woodworkers for a century, the exhibition is presented with the compliments of the trade delegation from the Alyina Merchant League that recently visited Kandersteg.

EMPLOYMENT OPPORTUNITIES

Recruitment Call

The Hounds of Harvest mercenary company seeks MechWarriors, qualified battle-armor infantry, and technicians for the company's maiden contract. Base compensation for combat elements (BattleMech or battle-armor squad) is a 1% share. Recruits with previous combat experience or who pass a combat-skills examination are eligible for a founder's bonus of one-half share, and those who furnish their own combat equipment receive an additional share.

Sign on at the hiring hall by 15 January. DropShip departs for Arc-Royal on 20 January.

Help Wanted

Seeking waitstaff, shift managers, and security guards for the new Ironsea Arms Hotel location at the Thun Spaceport. Get in on the

ground floor of the booming hospitality market. Competitive salary and benefits, plus tips. Candidates with experience in linguistics (Kandersteg English and Kandersteg Malay preferred), surveillance technology, and information analysis are especially encouraged to apply. We offer sponsorship for local immigration visas.

EVERYTHING UP THERE

ALAYNA M. WEATHERS

Everything is small from up there,
Secured behind helmet,
Gripping controls beneath a firm fist.
It takes some getting used to,
Propelling heavy feet forward—
Left, right, left, right—
Sunlight glinting off the visor.

Everything is different from up there,
Old names traded for new ones
As flesh becomes one with machine.
There's excitement at the little things—
A brand-new paint job,
Voices on the headset,
The firing of a gun.

There is the beginning,
When the only targets are for practice—
A great and temporary before.
Before the warfare,
Before the battle,
And everything is unstained from up there.

THREE WAYS HOME

TOM LEVEEN

PART 4 (OF 4)

CHAPTER THIRTEEN

TIERAPOLVO
TRAUSSIN
TAURIAN CONCORDAT
11 JUNE 2581
1328 HOURS

Toma's middle sister Rasha screams as she sees the giant BattleMechs bearing down on us. Toma and I scramble to tear away the brush concealing my *Griffin*. The instant I can reach the ladder, I grab it and launch myself up as fast as I can, bandaged hand and all.

I pop the canopy open and start smashing buttons and toggles to start the 'Mech. "Get them into the car!"

Rasha is already on her way toward the rusted-out passenger vehicle, seeking cover. She tumbles into the boxy back seat as Momai follows.

Metallic *tings!* jar my ears. Bullets. The *carcieta* 'Mechs aren't waiting for a clear shot, they're unloading now. The rounds coming at us are wild; the 'Mechs are too far away to aim properly, but it'll only take one shot to end someone's life.

"Come on, come on!" I shout as the battered *Griffin* whines and rumbles.

Rasha helps her mother into the vehicle. Momai chants something as she slides in, maybe a prayer. Below, Toma doesn't bother convincing his littlest sister to get into the vehicle; he slings an arm under Bita's shoulders and hikes up our BattleMech while she struggles against him.

No time for safety. I get the 'Mech moving before Toma and Bita are entirely into the cargo space. He shouts in alarm as he falls inside. I slam the canopy shut and turn the *Griffin* north, toward the decades-old skeletal vehicle, running as fast as the machine can go. Still on the move, I grab it with my BattleMech's left articulated hand. It won't be a comfortable ride for Momai and Rasha, but it'll have to be enough. Picking up the ruined vehicle isn't any different than lifting the hundreds of crates I've moved while on the front line. I can handle this.

Except, back then, I wasn't under fire, and my cargo wasn't human.

The Diamos *carcieta* 'Mechs—a *Stinger*, a *Wasp*, and a *Locust*—open fire again. The now-familiar sounds of machine-gun rounds banging into the rear armor make my passengers scream. Dust me, my back is right to the *carcieta*, they can't help but chip away at that thinner armor.

On each side of me, I can see the *Wasp* and the *Locust* splitting off. They're going to try flanking me. Light 'Mechs, but there's three of them, and my *Griffin*, though a medium 'Mech, is not in top condition.

These pilots aren't like the other three I faced earlier in the desert. They know what they're doing. If I stop to turn and lay into any one of the three 'Mechs, the other two can get behind me and tear me apart.

If I stop to turn...

"Hold on! This might hurt!"

Toma and Bita have no time to respond as I pull back hard on the throttle and slam on the jump-jet pedals.

My right hand flares in pain as I again ask too much of it. My stomach sinks and tickles, and my equilibrium spins as I launch the *Griffin*—backward.

The Diamos pilots must be so shocked at what they're seeing, because they stop firing. The *Stinger* behind me—now below me—shifts awkwardly on its feet, trying to track me.

We land in a crouch to absorb some of the shock. The moment we touch down, I let loose with my PPC, aimed at the *Stinger*'s right leg as it pivots toward us. The 'Mech's armor sparks and smokes as the spear of powerful energy slams into its upper leg.

My other two enemies turn and run toward us. The *Stinger* completes its turn and lowers its medium laser at my *Griffin*'s head. I'm looking straight down the pipe.

I hit the jump jets again, hoping I won't overheat after my backward leap.

The *Griffin* loves me: we leap up and right back down again, this time landing in front of the *Stinger*. Gritting my teeth, I pull the *Griffin* into a tight pivot, extending the 'Mech's right hand.

If I've timed this right—

My *Griffin*'s battlefist crashes into the 'Mech's shoulder and sends the machine toppling to the ground. The sound of the monumental spinning backfist hitting armor plating pierces my ears and makes my jaw hurt.

I scream in victory. It wasn't a fatal shot, but it must have put some fear into them.

More bullets and lasers ping into and off my *Griffin* from the sides. The other two 'Mechs are closing in. I'm tempted to swing my fist into the downed *Stinger*'s cockpit, but there's no time.

"They'll send more!" Toma shouts into my ear as if reading my thoughts.

He's right. Every second I spend here battling these goons is another second the *carcieta* will send more BattleMechs, vehicles, and men to stop us. We have to get off the X.

I turn north again, sending a PPC shot at the *Wasp*. They fire their laser back, tearing a hole in my 'Mech's right shoulder. But my energy weapon blasts a big enough hole in their left torso armor that they're forced to retreat.

I take the opportunity to sprint away. The *Locust* fires at me, but doesn't seem interested in continuing their pursuit. Not yet, anyway. Probably doesn't like the look of that PPC hole I just bored into their buddy.

Toma's right, though. More will come.

The desert rolls past outside as a few last rounds bang into the back of my 'Mech. I push the *Griffin* to its limit, baking us in all the heat the busted heat sinks can't purge. "Anyone injured?"

"We're all right," Toma pants. "You?"

"Fine." Not entirely true; I'm wondering if I've done permanent damage to my right hand.

Bita speaks, Toma translates. "My sister wants to thank you."

"Does she know the *carcieta* was coming for them?"

"Momai's known that since the day my father left. Bita doesn't understand. Hey, Ixy?"

"Yeah."

"You did it."

I grit my teeth. "We're not home yet."

"I know, but we made it this far—you *got* us this far—so whatever happens, you won't be forgotten. Are my mother and sister all right?"

I look down at the burnt-out car I'm carrying, fearful Momai and Rasha may have been hurt. But there they are, clutching the skeletal frame. Momai, as if intuiting my look, suddenly gives me a quick thumbs-up.

"They're good."

The *Griffin* is going as fast as it can over the unstable terrain. Occasionally it stumbles a little, but considering the beating I've put this 'Mech through, the *Griffin* is a real operator. The heat gauge is still high, but we haven't reached critical yet, so thankfully the remaining heat sinks are still working.

I straighten our path to head due north as best as possible. We're much farther west than where Toma and I first jumped the wall. We're completing the last leg of what amounts to a *u* shape through *carcieta* territory. Our current route, if left uninterrupted by *carcieta* or terrain, will take us very near Fort Erobern.

I wonder if that's going to be a problem.

"Hey...Toma."

"Yes?"

"I don't exactly have a plan for getting us back *in* to Erobern. So, I'm open to ideas."

"Because I'm a dusty ill?"

"Wouldn't put it that way, but yeah. How do we get outta here?"

I hear him shift in the back. "Well, there's a lot to think about. There are many places along the wall where Tierapolvos try to go over. But that means there's also likely to be a lot of *keyotes* nearby those same areas, dropping people off. Were you planning on jumping back over?"

"Kinda, yeah. I assume the same spot we came over is best, if it's the shortest height on this side."

"Do you think we can handle a jump that high, after what happened yesterday?"

"That part I don't know. I'm just kind of hoping at this point. But hope isn't tactical."

Toma doesn't seem nervous about the idea of the jump jets not being able to get us over the wall. "All right, and what if we can't figure out any other option?"

I sigh. "The best *I* can come up with? Conceal the *Griffin*, mark the coordinates, find a group of Tierapolvos going over, and try to go with them. Give the Taurian Defense Force the coordinates as quick as possible and let them send a strike team over to either bring the *Griffin* back or blow it up to keep it from the *carcieta*."

Toma whistles. "A lot has to go right to pull that off."

"Yeah. So, let's just pretend the jets are gonna work."

"Copy that."

It sounds like he grins. I don't.

We're still a long way from home.

We make good time before the *Griffin*'s heat gauge really starts to worry me. The 'pit is still a blast furnace, especially with so many bodies inside. If I'm baking up front in my cooling vest, Toma and Bita must be *dying* behind me. And we've all dragged the bitter odor of burning pop plants on our clothes with us. There's just no beating body heat. It's stifling.

"We need to stop," I say. "It's getting hot."

"Couldn't agree more," Toma says.

I scan the horizon for trees, anything to give us a bit of shade. It takes another twenty minutes until I find a tall-enough tree near the east side of a riverbed. No water, but at least we can get out and stretch, and let the 'Mech cool.

I take the *Griffin* as close to the tree as I can. The sun is setting. We still have a lot of daylight left, but at least it casts a decent shadow. Once I've got the 'Mech parked, I carefully set the rusted vehicle down and open my canopy. Bita manages to climb out on her own, under Toma's watchful eye, as Momai and Rasha creep out of their makeshift cargo box.

Toma hefts his pack as we all take a few minutes to roam a bit and stretch our legs. Rasha takes her little sister to a cluster of bushes.

"What's our water situation?" I ask Toma as he hands me a canteen.

"We brought some from the house. We always do, it's just instinctive. If we assume a straight shot with no problems from here to Erobern, we're good. If we have to veer east or west for a while for any reason, we'll be all right for a bit. If something really goes wrong, though, we have to take a long detour... This time tomorrow, we'd be in trouble."

I face north, taking another long drink. This time tomorrow? Things will definitely have gone wrong if we're still in Tierapolvo by then. On a straight course, we should reach the wall by nightfall.

"If you've got food, everyone should eat now, while we've got the water to digest it," I tell him.

Toma gathers his family under the shade and hands out bread and water bottles. I squint in the direction of home.

It's a goddamn miracle we're even alive.

The odor of the papaver smoke creeps into my nose from my clothing. My hand aches. My muscles are stiff and tight from so much combat in the 'Mech. And there are dead bodies out there in Tabin, lives that I took—

"Be right back." I jump into the shallow wash, walking quickly away from the family. I can feel Toma's eyes on me, but I don't hear him follow.

I walk a good distance away, farther than the bushes Rasha and Bita used. I don't want to get too far, but also need to be alone for a minute or two.

When the family is no longer in eyeshot, but I can still see the top of the *Griffin*, I spin and hunker behind a prickly cactus, twisting my shirt into a glove around my left hand and biting into the bandages on my right.

Then the shakes come.

Tiny squeaks whine deep in my throat. I can't close my eyes and can't unsee everything I've done since jumping over the wall. Blood spraying. Bullets flying. Metal tearing. My stomach tenses, turning to a plate of ice. My limbs quake, and still I can't shut my eyes. I can only stare, seeing but not seeing a little round pebble on the ground.

I suck in a breath, not by choice, but because my body forces it. It then seeps back out as if through a fist in my lungs, wheezing, like air from a punctured tire. I can't make my hands work, can't unclench them, can't tear my jaw away from the mouthful of dry and dirty bandages. Every muscle in my body grips tight around every bone.

We shouldn't be alive.

Any of us. How in the dusty hell we managed to get this far, I don't know. Luck, I guess. It won't hold forever. The options I gave Toma hardly constitute what a TDF special operator would call a plan. Some operator I'm turning out to be. I don't deserve to continue training, much less wear the uniform.

I lose track of time. Great; another reason I'd never make it as an operator. All I know is that at some point my jaw finally relaxes and I'm able to untwist my left hand from my shirt. The material stays in a rough, crumpled sphere where my fist had been. My breath slows, and I can blink again.

Glancing west, I realize we need to keep moving. Somewhere out there is a *carcieta* thirsting for our blood, and they're not going to stop till they get it. They must know we're heading north; if they have the resources, and I'm sure they do, they can form a skirmish line of 'Mechs, vehicles, and troops, and just sweep our direction like a net until they catch us.

My knees crack as I stand. I take one blissful moment to stretch all my limbs like we do before PT on the grinder, then walk back to the family.

Everyone's sitting under the tree. They're whispering, and I see it's because Bita has fallen asleep in Toma's lap, and no one wants to wake her. The image makes me pause in my footsteps and just look. Toma sees me, and smiles.

I smile back.

Then hear something.

So does he. Alarm strains his face.

I know the sound. But I know it too late.

Our bodies take over. I dive to one side, covering my head. Toma reaches out, grabbing Rasha and Momai into a huddle over Bita's prone, sleeping body. It's all he has time for.

Missiles slam into the *Griffin*. Armor fragments flies into the air, and my great war machine falls.

CHAPTER FOURTEEN

TIERAPOLVO
TRAUSSIN
TAURIAN CONCORDAT
11 JUNE 2581
1842 HOURS

The earth shakes as my reliable BattleMech is felled like a tree. It lands on its left shoulder, snapping off the armor pauldron, then topples face-up to stare at the sky, the canopy open like a mouth.

The children scream. Cloudy streaks hover in the sky, tracing the missiles' path. I get unsteadily to my feet and look toward Toma. The family seems safe—he is shoving them out from underneath the tree, away from my *Griffin*. Momai is wincing and working her jaw; the explosive sound probably hurt her ears. Maybe badly.

My *Griffin* smokes from a gaping hole in its left shoulder. If its legs are all right, maybe I can get it up and running...get into the battle...*the fightin's commenced.*

I bolt for the 'Mech while scanning for the source of the threat. When I see it, my heart shrinks in on itself—

—and gives me one last gasp of hope.

Leaping headlong for the cockpit, I scramble for the radio and shout desperately into it.

"This is Echo Zero-Zero-Two, Echo Zero-Zero-Two, hold your fire, I say again, hold your fire, mayday, mayday!"

I lift my head.

On the horizon west of us, the three Erobern BattleMechs who had—almost accidentally—bailed us out of the *carcieta* fight yesterday now march inexorably our way, arms and weapons up and pointed this direction. They're dozens of meters apart, making sure to not group together and allow for maximum maneuverability.

No response on the radio.

I hit the button again. "This is *Cadet Ixchel Marquez*, please respond! Hold your fire, hold your fire!"

The 'Mechs close in. By now, there's nowhere for me to run. I can only hope they won't fire on Toma and his family.

Still curled in the open cockpit, I watch helplessly as the three polished *Griffin*s surround me, their PPCs pointed in my face.

Silence. Silence but for the soft whistles and groans emanating from the three BattleMechs' inner workings.

I crawl out of the cockpit, raising my hands high. The muscles in my shoulders protest.

Nothing moves. The desert is still. The 'Mechs stare at me with expressionless canopies.

Then the cockpit of the center 'Mech opens. The MechWarrior takes off her neurohelmet and drops it in the seat as she stands.

"What in *the colossal dusty hell* are you doing out here, Ixy?"

Cornet Reina.

I don't know whether to scream, cry, or pass out. "Reina! Dust me, I'm so glad it's you..."

The cornet hikes quickly to the ground as the other two canopies pop open. I recognize Rev and Doc from our special forces unit. They too stand in their cockpits and look at me. Doc seems as furious as Reina, while Rev, the MechWarrior I'd fought alongside up north, sports an incredulous half grin on his face.

Reina marches to me and grabs my shoulders, scanning me top to bottom. "Damn, Cadet, look at you. What are you doing out here? You will tell me one hell of a story right this dusty second."

So I start the tale, as quickly as I can.

Toma and his family edge nearer. When I explain to Reina the risk they're facing, she stops me and barks, "Doc!"

Doc shimmies down his ladder with his medkit and strides to the family. Speaking in perfect—if unaccented—Tierapolvo, he gets them situated under the shade of the tree and triages them. Doc looks supremely capable right then, down on one knee, checking vitals, murmuring quietly with a reassuring smile. Somehow—*somehow*—he even has a small candy on a stick, which he gives to Bita. The little girl grasps it with a shy smile and starts chewing.

Reina listens to me intently, asking only a couple of questions. By the time I'm done, the sun is low in the west.

The cornet stands with her arms folded, glaring at the desert floor as if it's wronged her. "So you flagrantly committed theft of an armed Erobern military weapon and displayed its capabilities to an enemy force while intending to help illegal immigrants sneak into your own nation. That about the sum of it?"

"Um...yes, sir?"

When she replies, Reina's voice has softened. "And you've so far fended off three *carcieta* 'Mechs, and racked up at least one confirmed *carcieta* kill with a handgun while nursing a wounded gun arm."

"Well, I...! Yes, sir."

Reina looks up. "Well, dust me, Cadet, I'm glad you're on our side."

I release a breath. "How did you get here?"

"Your father sent us. And so far as I know, he has no idea who absconded with one of his precious 'Mechs, because our orders were shoot first, blow this 'Mech up second, and ask questions never."

My stomach flips. So that *is* why they fired on me. And I can't exactly complain. Militarily, it was the right call for my father to make.

"Why didn't you radio us when we jumped into that scrap yesterday?"

"I tried. The comm was already busted. I didn't have much choice but to run."

Reina looks into my eyes. "There's one thing you haven't told me. And that is *why*? What in the name of the unending universe could possibly compel you to do all of this, Ixy?"

And in that moment—it's not the first I've had with Reina—I almost tell her why. The real why.

Instead I shake my head. "Not now, sir. The Diamos are coming, one way or another, and we need to exfil."

Reina squints at me. She knows there's more.

Doc breaks the tension by appearing next to her. "All good, Cor'. The woman's probably got a busted eardrum and maybe a sonic concussion, and the boy's got some smoke inhalation. They've all got some mighty big bruises to look forward to from bouncing around in the cargo bay of a 'Mech and that scrapheap of a vehicle. Other than that, they're ready to roll."

He gives me a once-over, and finally his fierce expression forms a grin. "You, on the other hand, look like shit, Cadet."

"Thank you, sir."

Doc laughs loudly and claps me on the shoulder hard enough to make me take a step. "You better make it through selection, Ix. I want you in my squad!"

He climbs into his *Griffin* while Reina stands and fumes. Rev, still in his *Griffin*, scans the horizon. He catches my gaze and gives me a thumbs-up.

It almost makes this whole thing worth it.

"All right," Reina says. "Here's what we're gonna do. Rev!"

"Yes, sir?"

"Get on down here and fix this girl's radio if you can."

"Copy!"

Rev rushes to my BattleMech and begins tinkering.

Reina squares up to me again. "This mission is off the books entirely, which means all of *us* are off those same books. We need to get back to Erobern ASAP. We'll leave some water and gear for the ills, and—"

"We're not leaving them."

Reina's expression flashes shock before quickly shifting to anger. I have never in my life interrupted a superior officer.

"I don't believe I heard you correctly, Cadet."

"Sir, I am not leaving Toma's family behind. They're coming with us."

She *laughs*. "Cadet Marquez, you must have a concussion. I'm not bringing ills into our country."

"That's fine, Cornet, I'll do it myself if I have to."

She takes a step nearer and lowers her voice. "Is it the boy? You and he have a thing?"

I'm surprised it takes me a moment to answer. "Negative, Cornet. His family needs asylum to survive. I aim to make sure they have it."

"Then they should march on over to a crossing and apply like every other—"

"They already *have*, Reina. Their lives are in grievous danger. Right now, as we speak. There's no time for paperwork and appeals. If they don't get over that wall, they die. Or worse. So I would not be doing my duty to protect life if I left them behind."

"That oath applies to Taurian citizens, Cadet."

"Well, that's not how I see it, sir."

Reina stares at me for a long moment. I keep my gaze fixed straight ahead, arms at my sides.

She spits into the dirt. "You're prepared for every consequence coming your way?"

"I am, sir."

"That's easy to say here, when we're out-the-red."

"Easier to say when I'm back home and not being hunted by Tierapolvo *carcietas*, actually. Sir."

Behind her, Rev calls into my helmet mic, "Comm check, comm check," and Doc, in his open cockpit, giving a thumbs-up.

Rev nods my way and heads back to his BattleMech, calling, "Try not to fold, spindle, or mutilate anything back there. That radio's held together with hundred-k-per-hour tape and bubble gum."

Reina acknowledges, then folds her arms. "All right. We don't have time to bitch around this. We'll get this family to Erobern and into protective custody. What happens after that, no promises."

"But—"

"Shut up and listen, Ixy. We've got a long way to go. Let's get your 'Mech up and mobile and run for the border. Anybody gets in our way, we unleash hell. You keep running, and you jump that wall no matter what, you get me?"

"I get you, sir. Can't we let Fort Erobern know we're coming?" Of course, what I mean is Brigadier Adriano Marquez.

"Negative. Radio silence. We're on our own." Reina raises a hand and signals Doc and Rev to get ready to roll. They close their canopies and fire up their 'Mechs.

"Copy that," I say to Reina. "Thank you."

Her glare doesn't soften one bit. "Don't thank me yet, Cadet."

I stuff myself into my *Griffin* and get the gyro stabilized before attempting to stand the 'Mech back up. The *Griffin*—itself battered and bruised after everything I've put it through—gives me a few complaints, but eventually rises.

Reina waits until I'm up before climbing into her own *Griffin*. "I'm taking point, you're behind me, Doc and Rev in the rear. This old vehicle's useless—split the family into our BattleMechs. Hustle."

Toma and I quickly usher Momai into Reina's 'Mech, Rasha into Rev's, and little Bita goes with Doc, whom she clearly adores.

"What's the plan?" Toma asks as we get the family settled for the long ride.

"We go north," I say. "Fast. Jump the wall. Everyone goes into protective custody."

Toma frowns. "What's that mean? Like, prison?"

"No. Kind of a house arrest. I think. Honestly, I'm not sure. It'll be fine. Once we're back and I can explain everything to my father, it'll be all right."

"Well," Toma says as Rasha starts her climb, "To be honest, that all makes me a little nervous. But I also can't exactly say I don't trust you, can I?"

"Definitely not."

Toma chuckles softly and reaches for Bita to help her up Doc's ladder.

"*Nentay*, Toma!" She shoves his hands away, determined to make the climb on her own.

We watch her go, the candy stick still hanging out of her mouth.

Toma grins as she climbs, and glances at the other MechWarriors. "I feel better with them here."

"Me, too."

"A few more hours, and this'll all be over, right?"

"I sure hope so."

Bita topples into the cargo area with a squeal. Momai scolds her from Reina's 'Mech, and I imagine it's because of the stick poking out of her mouth. It'd be awfully sad for that little girl to choke on candy after all she's been through today.

Toma faces me and puts a hand on my shoulder. "Thank you, Ixy."

He is so sincere I can't respond. So I put my left hand on top of his, the one on my shoulder, and just nod—

Toma whips his hand off me, flinging it backward, and spits in my face.

Stunned, I try to make sense of why he'd be so kind to me one moment, then do this the next. I can feel the wetness of it on my lips.

Then the sound reaches my ears.

And Toma is on the ground.

His arm is gone.

CHAPTER FIFTEEN

TIERAPOLVO
TRAUSSIN
TAURIAN CONCORDAT
11 JUNE 2581
1933 HOURS

"*Toma!*"

He's alive, lying on his back in the dust, blinking. His right arm is several meters away, torn completely from his body.

The echo of the single gunshot echoes around us.

Carcieta. Diamos. Sniper. Near.

I drop, scanning the horizon. I can't see anything; no 'Mechs, no vehicles. But they're out there somewhere. At least one sniper team, well-concealed.

I low-crawl to Toma and try to get my arm under him. "Can you move?"

Toma's expression is dazed. "Ixy...?"

He's too big. Another shot sounds, *clanging* into the leg of my 'Mech. Instinctively I go flat, breathing in Tierapolvo dust.

Toma reaches for me. Grabs a handful of my shirt. His grip is like steel.

"Trap," he says as the color drains from his face. "Go."

"*Not* leaving you!" I pull him hard toward the ladder of my BattleMech. His family screams above us as my Erobern team hustles to close their canopies.

Toma coughs. "Go. Now."

"No!"

I drag him another few centimeters.

A third round blasts against my *Griffin*, just over my head, forcing me down.

"Trying to...pin you down...while their 'Mechs come. You have to *go*."

I lick my lips free of dust and blood—and realize he's right.

It hits me in a flash. The tactical reality we're in.

I'm strong, but not strong enough to pull someone his size up a vertical ladder. Even if I had the raw power, I couldn't do it quickly enough to avoid getting shot.

If I stay, one or both of us gets killed. Even as the other Erobern 'Mechs spread out in search of the shooter, they're relying on visual targeting—thermal won't help for another hour or more, after full sunset.

If I don't get into my *Griffin* and run, the Diamos will get Toma's family. They'll get these three special operators. They'll get me.

Toma's right. Who knows what kind of Diamos resources are headed our way?

"Toma..."

"Save them," he says, still clutching me.

"I'm coming back for you."

Toma's breathing becomes labored. "Three...ways home."

I take his hand off my shirt and squeeze it. "Three ways home."

Then I race for the ladder, screaming hate and rage at this damn country. What it does to people.

What it's doing to me.

A shot lands to my right. Then to my left. Then below me. Then I'm in. It was no trained gunman after all; an Erobern sniper would've killed me two minutes ago.

I yank the canopy shut and strap in. My radio crackles immediately.

"Ixy, you hurt?"

"No! Toma's down. I couldn't get him up, I couldn't—"

Rev breaks in over the radio. "Cor', I'm counting five—correction, seven—seven bogeys to the south."

"Make that ten," Doc follows. "Dust me, here they come. The fightin's commenced."

I move my *Griffin* away from the tree. Away from Toma. And spin south.

Now I see the *carcieta* 'Mechs. Dark shadows on the horizon, closing fast. No less than ten war machines.

"Cor'?" Doc says.

"Move out," Reina orders. "Fast as hell. Go!"

Fighting against the last image I have of Toma burned into my mind, I push the *Griffin* hard to the north. Everything I've got—everything I am and have been trained to be, I must focus on to get Toma's family to safety.

Reina leads the way, picking out a path among the bushes and boulders I never would have seen. Slight downhills to give our 'Mechs small but crucial bursts of speed, zigzags that are only taken when the path ahead would be too slow, always aimed north toward home.

Reina's voice hisses in my neurohelmet. "Marquez, how are your jets?"

Toma is still back there. Bleeding in the dirt.

"Cadet Marquez?"

Maybe there was something I could have done, some way I could have pulled him up and into the *Griffin*.

"Ixy, do you copy?"

Or stayed, stayed and fought, that's what I should have done, that's what I *should* do, go back now and fight those—

Something bangs into my 'Mech's shoulder. I jump and yelp, expecting to see smoke billowing from my *Griffin*.

No. It's Reina's BattleMech, walking alongside. She'd thumped my remaining armor pauldron with one giant 'Mech hand.

"Ixchel, are you copying me? Come in!"

"Y-yes. Copy."

"I know what you're doing in there, Cadet. Stop it. Right now. You did the right thing. But now you gotta put it away. You have a mission, you get me? The mission is what matters. Put him aside and deal with him later. That's an order."

"Yes. Yes, sir."

"How are your jets?"

I take a couple of deep, steadying breaths and push Toma out of my head with a silent apology to him. Then I check my gauges.

"Good. Far as I know."

There's a short pause before Reina says: "Ixy."

"Sir?"

"I'm sorry about the boy. Now let's get this done."

I let the radio fall silent.

A minute later it bursts to life again with Reina's voice. "How we doing back there, Rev?"

"Can't see 'em, but I don't think we lost 'em," Rev reports.

"Copy that," Reina says. "Everyone keep humping."

The sun slowly drops below the horizon on our left. My heat gauge steadily rises from the 'Mech's exertion, but more slowly than during the heat of the day.

I'm coming back for you, Toma. No matter what. One day I'll come back for you.

When the sun is down completely and the desert is engulfed by darkness, I switch to wireframe view and focus on Reina in front of me, setting a mean pace toward home. Roughly speaking, we should be able to reach the wall in another hour or so at this rate.

The wall. Home.

Two things I will never see the same way again, no matter what they do to me when I return.

And they *will* do something. It doesn't matter who my father is. He can't cover what I've done. He won't, even if he could. My father plays by the book, and for good reason. It's what keeps people alive.

Watching Reina run her 'Mech in front of me, the reality of my future settles into my heart. I won't ever be an operator with her. Or Doc, Rev, or anyone else. I won't be a MechWarrior. Not even infantry. If I'm not in prison, the best I can hope for is a dishonorable discharge from the cadet corps, which will then reflect on my father. Who knows what consequences he'll face, official or otherwise. The Concordat has many ways to punish people without official action.

I've destroyed what's left of my family.

"Bogey on our nine," Rev says on the radio, startling me.

"Bogey on our three," Doc adds. "Four. Five... Yeah, here they come, kiddos."

I suck in a breath and hit the thermal sensors.

To our right and left, the darkness is brightening. Black, then deep blue, then brighter blue. In another moment, the shapes will turn orange, then yellow, then white.

BattleMechs. And not the ten we're running from behind us. These are additional 'Mechs, closing in from other parts of the country. Word's out.

"What d'you wanna do, boss?" Rev says.

Reina takes a second. "Keep running. Let's see if we can put some distance between us. Nobody break off or open fire unless I say, get me?"

Doc and Rev affirm over the radio.

"Ixy? You get me?" Reina snaps.

"Um...yes, sir. Sorry. Copy that."

"You still with me, Cadet?"

"I'm with you, sir."

"Your job is to get over that border wall, no matter what. That is a direct order."

"Negative."

"...Say again?"

The certainty of my mission crystalizes. The others have Toma's family. I don't. They are the mission. I'm not.

"Reina, your order should be to get that family into Erobern. I'm expendable. If I wasn't, you wouldn't have shot at my 'Mech."

"Oh, no no no, Ixchel. I'm not going back to the brigadier to confirm your death."

"If it comes to that, tell him how we saved these people and that I love him. Marquez *out.*"

Reina doesn't respond. I think it's because in the end, she knows I'm right.

We keep pushing northward. The glowing masses on my canopy screen slowly get bigger even as they seem to slide behind me. Three distinct shapes take form on my right, then three more on my left.

They are not breaking off. They're charging ahead and closing like pincers behind us.

"Missiles!" Rev shouts into the radio. "They wanna do this!"

"Break-break-break!" Reina shouts.

We split up. The missiles hit the dirt just shy of Rev's 'Mech, throwing a ton of earth into the air. I imagine hearing the family screaming in fear. Dust me, they can't be in the middle of this anymore.

We push our war machines as hard as possible. The wall must be so close. If we can just keep going...

Another volley comes toward us. The small missiles fly over my head and hit the ground to the left of Reina, whose 'Mech jukes right in response.

"That was close!" Rev says, laughing. "We weapons free, boss?"

Reina growls into the radio. "We're still two clicks out. These dogs're gonna nip our heels every step of the way unless we hit 'em. Everyone, weapons free, fire at—"

"Negative!" I cry into my radio.

I say this because suddenly, in that moment, I understand everything Toma has tried to tell me about Tierapolvo:

Death *is* life here.

It suffuses every *aspect* of life. The *carcietas* see to that. The *carcietas* themselves, long at war with one another over pop and other illicit trade—including their trade in actual people—accept death as part of the job. And the civilians, people forced into working for the *carcietas* or else just trying to scratch out a living while keeping their heads down, have no choice but to acknowledge that this is how things work.

Dusty 'Polvo.

It's not that the women in our BattleMechs aren't afraid to die. It's that they've already accepted it as part of life here. If they were Erobern, if they were Taurian...I'd do exactly what Reina said and run hard for the wall. Instead, it's "Welcome to Tierapolvo," where it's better to put up your fists and die swinging than it is to run.

Because if you run, they'll just find you and make you wish you'd died.

These three women are ready. Even little Bita. They're warriors. Life here demands it. They're tougher than I'll ever be.

I just need to give my team space to get over the wall. And if I can also extract a little blood for Toma...so much the better.

Reina's voice is as sharp as a blade. "You are not in command here, Cadet."

"And I'm not a cadet anymore, Reina."

All four of our *Griffin*s are still running fast as Reina speaks. "This ain't about your future in the corps. This is about you getting your ass back to your father! Now go!"

"Negative, negative. The Diamos want me. They know who I am and what I've done. They're after me first. You all jump, I'll draw them off."

"You'll get killed, Ixy." It's Doc, his voice flat.

"So be it. Get that family to Erobern. Please. Marquez out."

"You were gonna be the best operator, Ix," Reina whispers over the radio. Then, loudly, she says, "All right, warriors. We're doing this. Jump for home in three—two—one—*break*!"

I skid to a halt, spin to face east, and start walking backward, launching salvos of missiles toward the pursuing 'Mechs as the other three *Griffin*s hit their jump jets.

The fightin's commenced.

CHAPTER SIXTEEN

TIERAPOLVO
TRAUSSIN
TAURIAN CONCORDAT
11 JUNE 2581
2115 HOURS

My missiles fly through the night sky. They cut white streaks across the thermal imaging on my canopy. The Diamos *carcieta* 'Mechs respond in kind, firing long-range missiles right back at me.

I rush forward to mitigate the attack. Maybe if I can disable the 'Mechs quickly, then turn to face the three from the west...

Two long-range missiles, fired from a *Toro* BattleMech in the center of the group, hit my *Griffin* in the torso, rocking me back. Thumping explosions sound behind me as the other three missiles impact the ground.

I lift my right arm and fire my PPC into a *Talos*, the 'Mech farthest to my left. Dust me, how did a *carcieta* get ahold of one of *those*? A dark spot appears on the yellow blob of its torso as we near each other—good hit. The *Talos* fires back, sending a deadly autocannon shot of its own toward me.

The shot misses, by a hair. I'm still up, but I can feel critical seconds ticking away. If the three westward 'Mechs behind me get within range, I am finished.

Time to shift tactics.

I hit my jump jets.

The *carcieta* 'Mechs fire at me as I go into the air. Laser beams and machine-gun slugs from the third 'Mech, a *Wasp*, tear into my right shoulder and lower legs, but most fly past. I land just beyond the *Talos*, which is in the middle of a pivot to face me.

Even as the *Toro* and *Wasp* keep firing at me, I swing the *Griffin*'s arm, bringing the full weight and speed of the battlefist to bear. The massive appendage comes down hard on the *Talos*' shoulder—taking it half off. The mechanical limb dangles from bent actuator pistons and sparking wires, its short-range missile launcher now useless.

Yes!

But more slugs from the *Wasp* nail my left side, and the *Toro* has me dead to rights with its particle cannon. The *Talos* in front of me stands stupidly for a moment, as if trying to figure out what just happened before waking up and jamming its autocannon into my *Griffin*'s guts.

I raise my left arm and point my PPC right into its canopy.

We fire simultaneously.

My *Griffin* groans as thunder echoes in the cockpit. My war machine crumples in the middle beneath the assault, like a person being punched in the stomach. Alarms blare around me, deafening. The blast actually knocks me out of the way of what would have been killing shots from the *Wasp* and *Toro*.

And as I fall back, the *Talos*' head evaporates.

The cockpit bursts apart like a firecracker in a piece of fruit. Sparks, showing white on my thermals, spray up out of its neck.

I see this moments before my 'Mech crashes backward to the dirt. My breath coughs out of me, straps pulling me taut against extant bruises.

I roll the *Griffin* to one side and climb back to its feet as more machine-gun rounds and lasers slam into my legs. I narrowly avoid a kick from the *Toro*.

If it's close enough to kick me...

With my *Griffin* on its feet, I swing the battlefist in a looping haymaker. It lands against the *Toro*'s shoulder, tilting my enemy on its feet. Fighting the momentum, I swing the opposite way now, bringing the *Griffin*'s clenched hand across the *Toro*'s cockpit in a backfist.

The *carcieta* 'Mech goes down like a whipped boxer—

And my *Griffin* stumbles down with it.

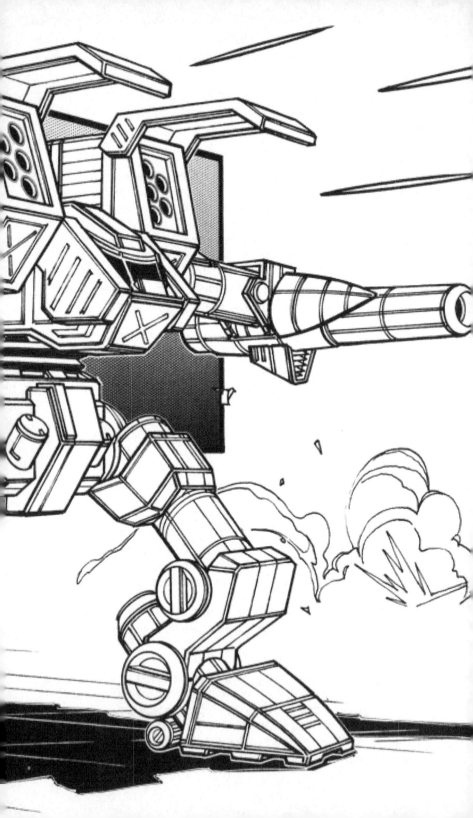

As we fall, the *Wasp* unloads great volleys of machine-gun fire at me. Screaming, I feel my *Griffin* taking the hits on its already-wounded torso.

I raise and fire the PPC in the last brief moment before crashing into the downed *Toro*, practically sitting on top of it. The wicked energy beam propels square into the *Wasp*'s center mass, and the BattleMech bursts apart like a torn doll.

Fighting for breath, I push the *Griffin* up and step backward, away from the carnage. All three Diamos BattleMechs are motionless.

Stunned that I'm still alive, I face south. In the darkness of my thermal, small bright spots are beginning to appear on the horizon.

The other ten 'Mechs we'd left behind. Maybe more.

I smash my missile launcher's firing stud multiple times, sending volleys at the approaching 'Mechs before running north. I won't hit much, if anything, but they'll know I'm still armed. It might slow them down just enough...

The Diamos BattleMechs fire right back. Long-range missiles fly at me from the rear. Most hit the dirt around me, but two bang into my feet.

I'm at an all-out sprint now.

No more missiles fly, but that's little comfort; the ten *carcieta* BattleMechs behind me are likely fully loaded with ammo—never mind an array of energy weapons—and if they can get within range, they'll shred me on the spot.

I spare a look back, using my 360-degree vision strip.

Three 'Mechs are in closer pursuit now, faster than the others. They must be the ones from the west who'd been closing. Either they can't quite keep up, or they're keeping their distance, waiting for the other ten to join them.

I don't want to know which. I switch to wireframe to better navigate the terrain, and that's when I see it:

The wall.

I'm here.

Or nearly so. I'm coming up on it fast. The spindly green lines outlining every shape on my screens show the tall concrete structure looming in the distance.

"Almost...home," I cough out. "Just hang on."

Five minutes later, I'm there. The border wall between Erobern and Tierapolvo stands like a monument before me.

And, as I tilt the head of my 'Mech backward, I also have to wonder if it's too high for my jump jets to reach.

Lasers bore holes into the concrete from behind me. One hits a shoulder actuator.

I hit the jumpers. My *Griffin* lurches off the ground. The rush of exhaust makes the cockpit rumble around me as the propellant is expelled from the ports.

Then the sound stops. It's like pulling the plug on a sound system.

My *Griffin* hovers barely above the top of the wall. I hit the maneuvering thrusters to get me over.

No response.

And now—falling.

Desperate, I stretch out the arms of my 'Mech. I crash into the wall on the descent, jarring my bruised, exhausted body. The top of the wall comes up fast, catching the *Griffin* under its arms.

I hang there for a second, like a cadet failing to clear an obstacle on the O-course. Then the weight of the machine begins dragging me down. Back into Tierapolvo.

Slugs and lasers ping off the back of my 'Mech and against the wall around me. My back is to the enemy, and I'm stuck here, unable to return fire.

This is where it ends, Ixy This is—

I focus on every scrap of training I've ever had. As shots continue slamming into my rear torso and the concrete all around me, I use the *Griffin*'s arms to try pulling myself over the top of the wall. I kick the 'Mech's legs, trying to find purchase against the smooth barrier.

Breathe, get air to your brain, solve the problem.

The entire purpose of a BattleMech is to handle the massive weapons loads they carry, and to negotiate a variety of terrain ground vehicles can't. I kick the *Griffin*'s legs again and give a hoarse scream as I push down with the 'Mech's arms.

Push 'em out and make 'em count...

Suddenly the center of gravity shifts, and my great war machine tumbles over the side of the wall and into Erobern.

The sound of my *Griffin* hitting Erobern soil vibrates my skeleton so hard, I'm sure it will split from my body. Everything is dark.

Time loses all meaning as I lie here in the cockpit of my BattleMech. At some point, I hear a faint dripping sound from somewhere deep in my machine. Soft beeps creep into my consciousness.

I open my eyes.

I'm alive.

All the months of training come back to me, and I tap the comm. No response. Rev said my radio was a mess; no surprise it's offline again.

Carefully, each muscle tense with pain, I get my *Griffin* up on its feet and point it toward Fort Erobern. I wonder if my team made it or not, and if Toma's family is safe.

Toma.

"Not now," I hear myself whisper. "Let's go home."

I march back to base, trying to make the *Griffin* run, but one or both of us just doesn't have the energy, and my heat gauge is in the red. I manage a clunky jog of sorts, all the way to the gates of Fort Erobern.

CHAPTER SEVENTEEN

FORT EROBERN
TRAUSSIN
TAURIAN CONCORDAT
12 JUNE 2581
0002 HOURS

The gates to Fort Erobern open. Someone in a control tower has seen my approach. Silently, I pilot my BattleMech onto base.

Everything is quiet. Peaceful. How long have I been gone? Feels like years. Switching my screens to natural light, there's plenty to see by under the orange streetlights and security lamps on the buildings.

This is home, but it's foreign somehow. I know where I am, but I don't recognize it.

Following the red paint on the ground, I go to the nearest 'Mech hangar, the same one I stole the *Griffin* from. Its gate is open, and I see Reina, Doc, Rev, and Toma's family all there, gathered in the middle of the floor.

They watch me back into a bay and power down the 'Mech. It feels like my body powers down with it.

I give the consoles one loving sweep of my hand. "Thank you, friend. You did good."

Then I open the canopy.

It's as if this action shakes the hangar into life. A small crowd gathers as I climb out. Techs, for the most part, and a few others in uniform. I see Blondie Boy—Cadet Jeffers—among them as my boots touch the deck. I'd expect him to be furious, because he must know by now that I duped him. Instead, he looks incredulous, like he can't believe I'm even here.

I go directly to Toma's family. Momai looks frightened but determined. Rasha has a steely glint in her eye as if awaiting an attack. And little Bita is smiling away like this has been a grand adventure.

I bend, stifling a groan, and ruffle her black hair. "Hey. You'll be safe now. All right?"

The little girl takes my hand. And I smile at her.

"Ixy."

It's Reina. I turn at the sound of her voice. "Reina, I—"

She's not alone. Flanking her, as if out of nowhere, are two men in military police uniforms. One of them withdraws icy steel handcuffs from a leather pouch.

"Cadet Ixchel Marquez," Reina says, her expression as smooth and cold as the border wall. "You are under arrest."

Reina takes the cuffs and snaps them on my wrists. Toma's mother and sisters look at us, shocked. Bita whines when the MPs gently separate our hands.

"Doc," I say as he and Rev watch with grim expressions. "Tell the girls I'm fine. This is scaring them."

Doc nods quickly. "Of course. Hey—I got this. I'll take care of 'em, Ix."

"Thank you."

Doc speaks to the girls in their native language as Reina and the MPs lead me out of the hangar and to a military vehicle with MP markings.

Reina opens the passenger door. I slide inside and watch through the windows as the cornet converses with the MPs. They all nod at one another, and the MPs hustle back into the hangar. Reina climbs into the driver's seat and closes the door.

"Where are they going?" I demand, fearing the answer. "What are they gonna do?"

"They'll take the family to medical," Reina says, starting the vehicle. "Don't worry, they'll be safe."

I lift my shackled wrists. "Sorry if I don't exactly believe you right now."

Reina faces me. The expression in her eyes makes me feel slapped. But I don't regret what I've said. I am Erobern. I am Taurian. I know how things work here. Or how I thought they used to.

Reina shakes her head a bit without a word, and she pulls away from the hangar.

I sit back, waiting for the justice buildings to come into sight. It's where the base's brig is, and where all the on-base legal work happens.

Only we don't end up there.

Reina drives to my house and stops. She pulls a key from her hip pocket and unlocks my handcuffs.

"You need to clean up," she says. "Let's go."

Reina climbs out, and I follow. She opens the front door for me, and I go inside.

I'm again hit by a dizzying sensation of familiarity and uncertainty. Everything is just where I left it, but it was so long ago.

Reina shuts the door.

"Is he here?" I ask.

"On his way. You should shower. Get some fresh clothes."

I force myself to walk down the hall to my room. I flick on the overhead light, and it blinds me for a moment. My bed, made, beckons. But I know Reina's right, I need to get clean.

She's standing in the doorway, leaning against the frame, hands in her pockets.

"Can I have some privacy?"

"Nope," she says. "Sorry. My orders are to not let you out of my sight."

"Whose orders?"

"Your father's."

Of course. I slide over to my bed and sit on its edge to unlace my boots. Somehow, the act of sitting there activates every wound I've gotten since jumping the wall into Tierapolvo. Every bruise aches, and my bones feel like shattered glass.

Reina comes in and browses my bookshelf while I undress. "Nice collection," she says, and turns. "Have you finished reading the—"

She stops cold when her eyes hit me. At this point, I'm wearing only my usual standard-issue black compression shorts.

Reina sighs quietly. "Dust me..."

I glance at my body, then realize I can only see so much. I limp and shuffle into my small bathroom, turn on the light, and face the mirror over the sink.

My eyes roam my body's reflection.

My skin is a discolored quilt of yellow, purple, and brown. My face is two shades darker than normal. I turn to examine my back; more of the same. Bruises, cuts, scrapes.

I've had some bad days in training, but I've never come home looking like this.

Leaning against the sink, I shove the door half-closed with one foot and unwrap my hand, which is almost twice its normal size. I turn on the narrow shower and step in. Hot water hits me, scalding, and I love it. It reminds me of the shower I took after the incident with Jeffers.

This shower is much better.

When I'm done, I get out and wrap a threadbare towel around myself. Reina has moved into the hallway outside my door, where she studies a picture of me, my father, and my mother, taken before her accident, before her addiction. We're at a fountain at the center of Fort Erobern, commemorating fallen soldiers.

Reina's back is to me. "I'm sorry your mother hasn't been here. She was an incredible woman. Strong."

"The pop was stronger."

"That stuff can get to the best of us, though. You really burned down a whole field?"

"Wasn't me. It was the *carcieta*, trying to smoke us out."

"Right," Reina says, and turns. "Well, in the report..." She trails off as she watches me straighten my dress uniform, the one reserved for special events and ceremonies. "Your Class A? How about some fatigues? Be more comfortable."

"This might be the last chance I get to wear it, don't you think? This is how I want to face him."

Reina is silent, but finally nods.

We go to the kitchen, where we sit at the table. I should be hungry—starving—but I'm not. "Reina—"

The front door opens. Every muscle in my body contracts.

He's home.

My father marches into the kitchen and yanks his cover off. Reina and I stand.

"Sir," she says.

"Cornet."

The brigadier stares at me, but doesn't stand too close. I keep my eyes fixed straight ahead. My father's jaw works in tight circles as he speaks to Reina. "How is...*the cadet*?"

I keep my mouth clenched tightly closed.

"Multiple bruises," Reina says, appraising me. "I assume a concussion or closed head injury. I don't know how bad that hand is. Some smoke inhalation from burning papaver plants. Doc said she needs a lot of rest, of course, and some tests on that thick skull of hers. But she'll live."

My father's hands curl into fists by his side. "And...how *else* is she?"

Reina spares me the briefest of glances.

"Sir, if I may speak freely? This cadet has performed admirably in the face of enemy fire. She's survived three contacts with the enemy, that I know of, and killed at least one enemy combatant during a small-arms exchange. She also single-handedly effected the rescue of three Tierapolvos—two children and their mother—who were under duress by the local *carcieta*. I'm no judge, sir...but I'd go into combat alongside this cadet any day of the week. She'd be earning a medal if we were at war with the 'Polvos instead of the SLDF."

"Only we're not," Brigadier Marquez replies.

Silence marches into the kitchen. None of us moves for a very long time.

"Cornet," my father says at last. "You and the cadet and the rest of your operator team will compile a report on this incident and have it on my desk twelve hours from now."

"Yes, sir."

"Nobody talks. Nobody says one dusty word. Keep those three 'Polvos isolated."

"Already done, sir. They're being held and treated in medical."

"Are they wounded?"

"Not badly, sir. Just banged around quite a bit. I've assigned Doc to keep the lawyers away. They'll be safe for a few days."

My father nods, once, tightly—as if his neck is on banded cords that snap his head back into place. "Very well. You have a lot of writing to do. Get back to your post."

"Sir." Reina snatches her cover from one pocket, steps toward the hall, and walks out of the house, closing the door softly behind her.

My father turns his attention back to me...stares...then sighs and slumps into a chair.

"I got a full report from Rev. I don't imagine there's anything you wish to add."

"Probably not, sir."

"Ixchel. You could have started a war."

"Sir, I—"

"Quiet. You need to know where things stand right now. We are all lucky beyond belief that you didn't encounter any actual 'Polvo military. They would have been honor bound to make an international incident of it. Rightly so. Your recklessness could have pulled this entire nation into a conflict that I assure you would have taken the lives of hundreds or thousands. The fact that all your encounters were with *carcietas* is a small blessing. So *fortunately*—and I use that word loosely—the real factor here is that you stole a BattleMech and illegally brought immigrants into our country. Those two facts alone are enough to imprison you for most of your natural life. Do you understand that?"

"Yes."

For some reason, my answer makes his face flush red. "Did you understand it *before* you did it?"

"Yes, I did."

My father stands so fast and furious the chair spins backward and crashes against the stove with a clatter. I don't flinch.

"But you did it anyway! Everything *you* have ever worked for and everything *I* have ever worked for is now at risk! If the Concordat wants my head, they're gonna have it. That puts the mission we were working on at risk. You didn't just risk your life, you risked the lives of operators. *My men!*"

I say nothing.

My father paces in front of me like a drill sergeant. "I know things have been difficult for us. I know our lives are not proceeding the way we'd both hoped. And *off* the record, I for one am glad you were able to stuff a few rounds down the throats of those dusty *carcietas*. But Ixy...why? Why would you put yourself through this? What reason could you have for ever choosing to do something like this?"

He lunges suddenly and grabs me by the shoulders. "Speak! What do you have to say for yourself?"

I meet my father's eyes. "You do not want to know."

He lets go of me and takes one step back. He puts his hands behind him in parade rest, his eyes blazing. "Cadet Ixchel Marquez...I am ordering you to explain to me why you chose this course of action. Answer me."

I never told Toma why I was helping him; my friend, Toma, who right now is either dead or in some *carcieta* hell I can't even imagine. Who gave himself up for his family, a family that lived under a cloud of fear for no other reason than where they happened to be born. I think of little Bita, and of Rasha, and I know for the time being, they are safe. That their safety is worth anything Erobern wants to do to me. I see Momai's proud face, her willingness to endure and keep fighting no matter what.

I'm only a cadet. But I have served in the company of warriors.

Looking into my father's eyes, I tell him the truth I have kept secret for five years.

"Sir.

"When I was twelve years old, I went to a party in the desert with several cadets and soldiers. It was the weekend after Mom passed away, and I wanted to forget what she looked like as she died. It got late, and I wanted to go home, but everyone was too high on pop to take me. Then finally one cadet offered to walk me home. I said thank you. Only instead, he took me into the desert. When we were alone, he tore my clothes. Put his hands on me. Forced me to the ground.

"I tried to make him stop, but I wasn't strong enough to get him off me. So as he was trying to...as the cadet attempted...I found a rock. Just within reach. I picked it up and hit him in the head. He fell off me. I hit him again. And then I did it again and again until he was dead. I left him there, and then I walked home alone.

"You weren't here. I called Central Command, and they wouldn't put me through. Said you were planning a mission and couldn't be reached.

"Except for me, everyone at the party was taking pop, so they didn't remember much. I'm sure they weren't going to admit to having a party anyway, or to taking pop. I assumed someone would find him, but I don't think anyone did. I don't know his name, but you can look him up. He'll be listed as AWOL for the past five years.

"I have never told anyone what happened that night. But now there are three women who won't have to live through it like I did.

"And I would do it all again.

"That's what I have to say for myself.

"Sir."

My father stares at me, unblinking, for an eternity. I know he has to take me into custody now. And I am fine with that. We all have our duties.

I've done mine.

"Come here," he says.

I step to Brigadier Adriano Marquez and stand at perfect attention. "Sir."

My father looks down the length of my body as if to inspect my uniform, which I know to be in perfect regulation. When he looks up again, his eyes shine.

Carefully, slowly, he wraps his arms around me and holds me so close I can barely breathe. A sound I have never before heard from him comes out of his mouth.

My father is weeping.

All my strength—all my training—washes out of my body and I hug him back, tight.

Holding one another for the first time since my mother died, we weep together. And I am home.

AUTHOR'S NOTE

Thirteen is the average age of a child first exploited for sex trafficking. My home state is one of the biggest areas in the United States for human smuggling and trafficking. It is a very real and ongoing problem. To learn more about how to help the girls and women being affected, please visit:

www.streetlightusa.org

NO HARD FEELINGS:
HOW TO MAINTAIN PROFESSIONALISM WHEN YOU KILL PEOPLE FOR A LIVING

WUNJI LAU

THESSALON BROADCAST COMPLEX
STUDIO 5
GALATEA
ISLE OF SKYE
22 FEBRUARY 3152

[Transcript of *The Headkick* talk show]

Murphy Chord: It's said the relationship between mercenary and employer must be grounded in mutual trust. Wise words, and the topic for our next group of guests. I'm Murphy Chord, and tonight on *The Headkick*, we have with us five people who, as always, have no idea who they're about to share the stage with. Lights up! Introducing Serina Arkhan from the Professional Soldiery Liaison office of the Draconis Combine! Colm Alseides of the Furballers mercenary unit! Zander Villamontes from the Mercenary Liaison division of the Federated Suns! Lillianella von Heidelflügel III of the Kraken Unleashed mercenary unit! And Merchant Commander Gerio from Clan Sea Fox's Tiburon Khanate!

Gerio: I am honored to be here.

Zander Villamontes: Yeah, likewise.

Lillianella von Heidelflügel III: Good evening, all.

Murphy: So, let's get started. In the violent and often literally cutthroat business of war, how is it that all of you, and others like you, can live and work alongside each other?

Serina Arkhan: Civil relationships are vital to any business, military or not. Colonel Villamontes' office is only a few blocks from mine, and we see each other at municipal and civil defense meetings all the time. We also work with many of the same vendors, especially under the, *ahem*, current market conditions in the region. For example, both of us have meetings with Captain von Heidelflügel this week. Yes, our nations are at war, bitterly so. My own home city was recently destroyed. But in this environment, with these assignments, the only way we can perform our duties is by avoiding unnecessary acrimony with local representatives who are far removed from the conflict.

Zander: Right on, Serina. We're trying to hire the best troops we can, and a big part of that is showing that we can be even-tempered, reasonable, and considered in our actions and comportment, regardless of the tragedies that affect everyone on all sides.

Colm Alseides: That goes for us mercs, too. It's kind of inevitable that conflicts occur, since the nature of the job means it's fairly common to find that someone you've shared drinks, a table, or a barracks with on a previous contract is now shooting at you. We had a tangle with Kraken Unleashed a few years back, and in the last scrum, my wife took a hit to the cockpit. Yet today, Lillianella and I are about to ship out on the same side, and I'm cool with it. Don't get me wrong, I was in a bad way for a long time, but people are relying on me. If we can't *do* the job, we don't *get* the job.

Lillianella: And you know I'm sorry for your loss, Colm. That entire raid was a cock-up from the start. I know that sayings like "It's just business" are common in holovids, but the reality isn't far from that. We all have bills to pay and mouths to feed, and swallowed bile is among the least of the sacrifices we all make.

Zander: We also try to be cognizant of familial and cultural links. Most contracts have terms covering contingencies when an engagement might involve relatives or other conflicts of interest, permitting varying levels of leeway in such circumstances.

Colm: Merc units also have internal policies like that, maybe letting you sit out a job if, for example, your brother is on the other side. But the legalese gets slippery, and most people who can't afford legal aid don't read the fine print. Still, it helps to keep grudges from happening, at least in theory.

Murphy: But there are famous cases of generational grievances and blood feuds, yes?

Lillianella: Certainly. But vendetta is a luxury reserved for units with the wealth and clout to support that sort of childishness. Behavior like that seldom ends well. Everyone has heard of Wayne Waco and his feud with Wolf's Dragoons, but there are countless less-fortunate mercenaries who died because of an obsessive feud.

Gerio: And for our Clan's part, we not only enforce peace at our trade events and depots, we provide forums for discussion, reconciliation, and maintenance of professional perspectives. We recognize the challenges in marketing our products fairly and equitably to all customers, and work hard to foster cordial relations among all parties. After all, our culture prizes the importance of moving on from the last fight to better prepare for the next.

Colm: Yeah, the Foxes are real good at covering their butts. Most transactions, the "product" is disabled until they hit orbit, so they don't have to worry about customers getting rowdy or greedy while they're in the line of fire.

Gerio: Thus also ensuring a safe and enjoyable experience for all. I would hope we all can appreciate a safe zone for building trust between all parties.

Serina: Yes, long ago, the Mercenary Review and Bonding Commission used to keep tabs on mercs and enforce at least some good behavior. These days, everyone's got to rely on slow word of mouth. A rogue merc outfit can get away with war crimes for months.

Lillianella: Or an employer can use the delay to manipulate funds and logistics, too. Company-store schemes are just as much of a threat to mercenary independence as they used to be—

Serina and Zander (simultaneously): *Untrue.*

Lillianella: —but with a different dynamic. With no MRBC or ComStar, there's no authority to appeal an unfair contract to, but there's also less fallout from leaving a contract when terms are pushed too far.

Colm: Even back then, it was pretty common for an employer to use mercs as patsies and get away with it scot-free. Sure, big names like the Gray Death Legion traded on their stories about sticking it to turncoat employers, but for every legend like that, there are dozens, hundreds more units that just have to suck up whatever scapegoating their employer puts on them.

Zander: Bullshit. If that happened as much as you claim, no one would take jobs with us—um, I mean, those employers.

Colm: Lucky for you, pal, there's always plenty of desperate people willing to take an iffy contract to stay solvent. Those people usually end up getting stuck with a choice between doing dirty work or not getting paid.

Murphy: Not to be blunt here, but isn't dirty work part of the job?

Colm: Within limits. Yeah, there's always a chance you'll get in a scrap with local civilians. Sure, you can try to specify deployment and drop areas, but you can't force the opposition to act the way you want. If they want to fight it out in a residential area, you don't have many options. It sounds callous, but you learn to walk away from the fight when it's done, without looking back. We don't have the spare cash to pay reparations, and believe me, the last thing survivors want is to hear apologies, thoughts, or prayers from the people who just stomped their homes flat.

Lillianella: Also, common contract language has rigorous disclosure restrictions regarding the media.

Zander: Those contract terms are there to prevent mercs from using public opinion and media firestorms to fraudulently claim damages or promote themselves at our expense.

Lillianella: It also *conveniently* means mercenaries are guaranteed to get blamed for anything that lowers public opinion, especially regarding property damage and civilian casualties. Using the "just following orders" excuse does little more than get a unit labeled with terms like "amoral" and "murderous."

Colm: The Dracs may spin the news into something pro-Kurita, and the Feddies may just do a complete media blackout, but either way, those cities are still leveled. And you can bet that in both cases, whether those places get rebuilt is entirely dependent on which noble has favor and how many 'Mech parts the place turns out.

Serina and Zander (simultaneously): *Untrue!*

Zander: You still get paid, don't you? And I think we all know that having "amoral" and "murderous" on your résumé is actually a plus in a lot of places.

Colm: Except we're not murderers, unlike some House bootlickers I can mention—

Murphy: Okay, okay. So, it sounds like if contracts are no protection for either party—

Serina: We're back to building trust and accepting certain risks.

Gerio: The Sea Foxes do offer escrow services to ensure payment and fair treatment.

Colm: For a big ol' percentage.

Gerio: Of course. But we hope the possibility of added expenses or reduced lines of credit with our merchants will be sufficient deterrent for malfeasance. For example, our past assistance on Hall helped prevent Serina from having to blacklist a unit with an otherwise excellent record.

Serina: Please. We could have handled that ourselves. We're a long way from Coordinator Takashi's "Death to Mercs" policies. Blacklisting helps no one except in the most egregious of circumstances.

Lillianella: Wait. Hall was *you*? I got demoted to a desk on this rock because of your crap intel!

Serina: Ah. Well.

Colm: So on Hall, *you* were the one who sent the Kraks to those coordinates? My wife *died* because you couldn't read a map right?

Murphy: Sooooo, about that. I think it's time we bring out our surprise guest. Introducing Margaret Alseides!

Colm: The hell? Maggie? You're *alive*?!

Margaret Alseides: Hi, Colm. You're looking well.

Colm: Lill, you knew about this?

Lillianella: No! Murphy, what kind of stunt is this?

Colm: Maggie, how—

Margaret: I got picked up by a SAR team. Sea Foxes. Been there ever since. Gerio and I figured it was time for you to know—wait, "Lill?" Are you with HER now? She *shot* me!

Colm: You and Gerio? You chose this vatfreak over coming home?

Gerio: Colm, I promise, Margaret is quite happy with us. Indeed, this is exactly the kind of situation that requires expert mediation and therapeutic advice, which Concordia Counseling—

Margaret: Oh, Gerio, come off it. You're in this too. I mean, you were the one who sold Serina's family's location to that guy over there.

Gerio: Wait. What? My love, what are you doing?

Serina: Zander? *You*. You had my hometown burned. Fedrat scum. I'm gonna kill you.

Colm: "My love?" Oh, there's about to be fricasseed Clanner on the menu tonight.

Lillianella: Come back here, Serina. You owe blood to my lancemates.

Zander: Ladies, please—ow, oh god, not in the face!

Murphy: Aaaaaaand now for a word from our sponsor, Concordia Counseling and Mediation Services of Galatea. Keeping peace by building—and rebuilding—trust. We'll see you all after the break—

[*Colm throws his chair in Gerio's direction. Gerio ducks. The chair strikes the camera and cracks the lens.*]

PLANET DIGEST: RAHWAY II

ERIC SALZMAN

Star Type (Recharge Time): G6V (187 hours)
Position in System: 2 (of 6)
Time to Jump Point: 7.01 days
Number of Satellites: None
Surface Gravity: 0.91
Atm. Pressure: Standard (Breathable)
Equatorial Temperature: 45°C (Desert)
Surface Water: 13%
Recharge Station: None
HPG Class: None (3150)
Highest Native Life: Reptile
Population: 20,000 (as of 3150)
Socio-Industrial Levels: B-D-C-D-C (3150)
Landmass (Capital City): Besplodniye (Mirgavan)

Rahway II was passed over when Tikonovian nobles established its sister planet, Rahway III, as the resort world of Sonnia in the early 27th century, amid a boom in interstellar tourism. Whereas Sonnia featured lush tropical jungles and ample water, Rahway II was mostly barren. Its proximity to the system's yellow-dwarf primary meant the predominant landscape was scorched wasteland incapable of supporting life. The northern and southern polar regions were livable, even pleasant, but the habitable zone was judged too small for agricultural self-sufficiency, while exploitation of mineral resources was considered uneconomical.

Capellan forces captured the system during the First Succession War, quickly overrunning Rahway II's northern polar listening post. House Davion reclaimed the system as part of Operation Sun in 2829, scourging the Capellan presence from Rahway II. The Armed Forces of the Federated Suns subsequently established a substantial military base there, Fort Damien Hasek, adjacent to one of the largest bodies of water on the barren world. For the next two centuries, Rahway II served as a staging point for AFFS strikes into the Capellan Confederation.

Whereas First Princes Andrew and Ian Davion distrusted mercenaries, limiting use of their services in the waning years of the Third Succession War, Hanse Davion aggressively recruited such units following his ascension in 3013, seeing them as the key to breaking the centuries-long stalemate. To attract the best units, Hanse offered landholds, large mission bonuses, and independent command rights. At the tempo of high-mobility operations he envisioned, Hanse recognized that mercenaries would need somewhere to recover. He therefore directed the Department of Mercenary Relations to convert Rahway II into a dedicated rest-and-recuperation world.

Located at the coreward tip of the Capellan March, the Rahway system proved a convenient post-mission R&R destination for Davion mercenaries striking at targets in the Capellan Confederation and the Draconis Combine. By 3020, the initial conversions had been completed, and Fort Damien Hasek became the Mirgavan Resort Complex. Duke Michael Hasek-Davion presided over the grand opening (sullenly forced by Hanse to officiate at the removal of his ancestor's name).

Mirgavan retained the spaceport and hangar facilities, along with 'Mech bays and vehicle garages where maintenance could be carried out

by trained AFFS technicians—a major draw for units lacking sufficient support staff. The barracks were replaced with a Golden Star-branded hotel/casino, while the mess hall became a cluster of free-standing taverns and restaurants offering cuisines from across the Inner Sphere. The hospitality industry on Sonnia rotated staff to Rahway II on month-long shifts, including professional escorts to staff a red-light district.

Though not intended by design, many of the bars and eateries quickly became semi-exclusive hangouts for different service branches. Technical support staff congregated at the Malfin' Mackie, a retro Terran Hegemony-themed alehouse a short walk from the 'Mech bays. Tankers rubbed shoulders with their peers in Lavrinenko's Tea House, though hovercraft crews preferred the ambiance at The Burlingrad, an exclusive skybox restaurant atop an enclosed hoverdrome. MechWarriors regarded Maloof's Tavern as the perfect place to swap stories of their battlefield exploits over platters of tabbouleh, falafel, and shawarma. Gwyddfa Rhita became the exclusive domain of infantry, sporting the severed head of a Capellan *Firestarter* over the door. Ship crews and fighter pilots selected the Flying Tiger Roadhouse as their preferred gathering spot, both for its incomparable shrimp curry and its beautiful garden-dining setting. Dozens of other establishments welcomed soldiers of all stripes, but it quickly became a hard taboo for a non-member to enter one of the exclusive hangouts without a formal invitation.

While all mercenaries under Davion employ were entitled to book time on Rahway II, the Department of Mercenary Relations began offering all-expenses-paid stays as part of contracts for high-intensity raids and other heavy action. As the resort's reputation grew, rank-and-file troops pressured their commanders to cede ground on command and salvage rights in favor of trips to Rahway II, especially if it meant their battered 'Mechs could get repairs and refits often unavailable in the field.

The draw of Mirgavan led to greater competition for Davion contracts, ensuring the AFFS launched the Fourth Succession War with high-quality mercenary support. Once the Federated Commonwealth unification began, Rahway II was opened to units in Lyran service as well, though most opted for the closer options on Solaris VII, Dustball, and Kooken's Pleasure Pit, preserving Mirgavan's identity as a uniquely Federated Suns mercenary haven.

Following the Clan invasion, in 3053 the Department of Military Relations heavily invested in improving the amenities on Rahway II to incentivize mercenaries to take high-risk raids into Clan-held territories. This expansion added comprehensive medical treatment facilities (including mental-health counseling); fitness centers; sprawling sports complexes; a state-of-the-art holotheater; a concert pavilion; golf courses; tracks for motorcycle, sportscar, and skimmer racing; wilderness trails; and wasteland dune-buggy excursions. Hunting expeditions and safaris launched from a wilderness lodge at the undeveloped southern pole. The New Avalon Institute of Science also opened an educational center, offering classes in repair and maintenance, briefings on recovered *lostech* and new weapon systems, and tactical reviews of Clan technology capabilities. The center also offered classes in art, photography, holography production, and crafts, as well as studios and workshops for independent practice.

Though brawls between drunken revelers were not uncommon, actual combat on Rahway II has been rare, thanks to a strong military-police detachment. During the FedCom Civil War, however, tensions rose between pro-Katherine and pro-Victor commands sharing space at Mirgavan. In 3063, recruiters for Marshal Nathaniel Hasek called on vacationing mercenaries to join the Allied defense of Kathil, and several commands prepared to deploy, swearing loyalty to Victor's faction. Katherine-loyalist elements of the Osaka Mercenary Legion, incited by Loki agents, attempted to seize the spaceport and 'Mech bays to prevent the pro-Victor mercenaries' departure. However, the Black Cats infantry battalion reinforced the military police, enabling the Victor-supporters to reach their 'Mechs. The ensuing battle raged across the spaceport and spilled out into the badlands beyond before the Legion accepted defeat.

The formation of the Word of Blake Protectorate made Rahway a front-line system during the Jihad, giving exhausted anti-Blakist mercenaries a place to rest between campaigns. Following a devastating mercenary attack against the Earthwerks facilities on Tikonov in October 3074, the Word of Blake's First Division launched a retaliatory strike against Rahway II with Ring of Fire III-beta in December. The vacationing mercenaries, several of which had participated in the action on Tikonov, aggressively engaged the Blakist raiders in high orbit, forcing their DropShips to land in the desert wastes outside of Mirgavan. Mercenary 'Mech forces attempted to overrun the Level III's landing zone, but Precentor Debra Hale's troops held firm and successfully breached the mercenary lines, sending a Level II of infantry into Mirgavan itself to take dependents and support personnel hostage. Mercenary infantry and military police fought side by side in defense of the noncombatants, breaking the Blakist thrust at Maloof's. With Hale's failure, she and her surviving troops retreated to Tikonov.

In 3146, en route to Marlette, Julian Davion's Task Force Panoply arrived in the Rahway system and called on all Federated Suns mercenaries there to join him in his campaign to push back against the Capellan Confederation's invasion. The assortment of small and medium units unanimously elected to join Julian, substantially augmenting his forces.

TERRAIN TABLES

To randomly determine the mapsheets for a battle set on this planet, choose the region, then roll a D6 and select the map matching the result. The maps in this list can be found in the noted map set (MS), map-compilation set (MC), or map pack (MP).

Mirgavan
Note: The Mirgavan complex is densely built up.

1: DropPort #1 (MS 7)
2: DropPort #2 (MS 7)
3: Military Base #1 (MS 7)
4: Military Base #2 (MS 7)
5: City (Downtown) (MC 2)
6: City (Suburbs) (MC 2)

Wastelands
Note: Scorched and lifeless, it is too hot for liquid water to exist in the wastelands. Replace all water hexes with clear, and all woods hexes with rough terrain.

1: Desert Sinkhole #1 (MC 1)
2: Desert Sinkhole #2 (MC 1)
3: Sand Drift #1 (MP Deserts)
4: Sand Drift #2 (MP Deserts)
5: Desert Mountain #1 (MC 1)
6: Desert Mountain #2 (MC 1)

Poles
Note: The polar regions feature a mild climate with unspoiled lakes, hills, and forests surrounded by a belt of scrublands that gradually turns to barren desert badlands.

1: Lakes (MP Grasslands)
2: Woodland (MP Grasslands)
3: Heavy Forest #1 (MC 1)
4: Heavy Forest #2 (MC 1)
5: Streams (MP Grasslands)
6: River CommCenter (MP Grasslands)

FOOLPROOF

JAMES BIXBY

**HEARING AS TO THE SUITABILITY
OF THE HEAVY GAUSS RIFLE
1 OCTOBER 3059**

Bench officers: names redacted
Lyran Alliance Armed Forces liaison to Defiance Industries:
    Leutnant-General Thomas Hogarth

[Begin transcript]

Bench Officer 1: General Hogarth, official documents continuously refer to you as both a liaison to Defiance Industries and a consultant. Is that correct?

Leutnant-General Thomas Hogarth: Yes, it is.

Bench 1: And in that time, how many projects have you "consulted" on with Defiance Industries?

Hogarth: In 3043, I was a supervising consultant on the development for the Condor Trans Track concept tank, which proved so successful that the Armed Forces of the Federated Commonwealth delivered a full battalion of them to combat formations...

**TRANS TRACK LAUNCH PARTY
PANDORA
FEDERATED COMMONWEALTH
27 OCTOBER 3045**

"This revolutionary new system will allow the Hover Cavalry formations of our new alliance to overcome otherwise impassable terrain," the

Defiance Industries hype man said before the crowd. "Each hovertank so equipped can extricate itself, should its more mobile skirts collapse, safeguarding the lives of the crew. Generals of the AFFC, I present the Condor Trans-Track!"

A curtain dropped and revealed an otherwise standard-looking Condor hovertank, braced on the front and back by clearly visible steel frames. The polymer lift skirt was being filled by an adjacent fan-and-tube system rather than its onboard engine. Every few minutes the skirt would deflate and retract, revealing tank treads beneath. The mockup showed how the machine was supposed to work. It was all just a matter of resources, as far as Thomas Hogarth was concerned.

"So, Kommandant Hogarth!" General Redburn shook the younger officer's hand. "When can we expect to see a field demonstration?"

"Oh, soon, I expect, General. There are some kinks that still need to be worked out—"

"Kinks?"

"This is still an experimental system, General Redburn. The conversion system is delicate. We can get it to work reliably in the lab and even the hangar, but we are working on the needed structural reinforcements for field trials. We don't want stuck tanks while out on maneuvers, do we?" Kommandant Hogarth slapped the general's shoulder.

"Trust me, when we deliver the first battalion of these, the system will work, guaranteed!"

HEARING AS TO THE SUITABILITY
OF THE HEAVY GAUSS RIFLE
1 OCTOBER 3059

> **Bench Officer 2:** As I recall the system never worked. Each of the vehicles manufactured got shifted around until they all wound up back in your command. Stuck in their treaded configurations, according to reports.
>
> **Bench 1:** And from what I understand, the already light weaponry had to be downgraded to provide the necessary mass for the nonfunctional system.
>
> **Hogarth:** It was merely a concept. This very body determined that I could not be held responsible for enthusiastic procurement officers.
>
> **Bench Officer 3:** Let's move on to this current project, code name Hammerfist.

Hogarth: Yes, the heavy Gauss rifle. Its standard cousin was already enthusiastically greeted by the AFFC. It gives our troops a great equalizer against the Jade Falcon and Steel Viper Clans who continue to occupy our worlds in the Tamar March.

Bench 1: Spare us the patriotic fervor, General. You are here to discuss your lack of progress.

Hogarth: Of course. The concept was very simple. We wanted to fire a larger projectile at the same velocity as a standard Gauss rifle.

Bench 1: According to your design documents, there is a hand-drawn image of an *Atlas* firing a hip-mounted gun, with a large blast coming from the barrel and the note "MORE POWER!"

[*Hogarth chokes on a sip of water, then whispers to counsel.*]

Hogarth: I do not have that document in front of me, ma'am. Anyway, our goal was to maintain the relative mass and size of a standard Gauss rifle while using a larger projectile to double the damage output. In theory, it should work...

AFFC GENERAL OFFICERS COUNCIL
THARKAD PALACE
THARKAD
17 OCTOBER 3055

"I am telling you, Tom, this will never work," Kommandant Adam Steiner said, the frost evaporating slowly from the schnapps glass in his hand.

"Adam, my boy," Thomas said, "don't let your successes blind you to the possibility." He slapped the newly minted hero of the Commonwealth on the shoulder. "It is just a matter of physics. More mass means more energy, that's all. A BattleMech's fusion reactor can handle the load."

"It may handle the load, General," said a short-haired woman in a white evening gown, "but the specs you're talking about are just inadequate." Her right hand was gloved all the way to her elbow, and a pair of snifters dangled between her fingers. "For such a weapon to handle the power load, you would need at least fifty percent more capacitors, not to mention reinforcement of the barrel, breech, and mountings. You are looking at a thirty percent increase in mass, minimum. Not to mention the drop in range."

"Madame Specter—" Thomas said.

"Rachel is a captain now, Tom, and I expect you to address her as such," Adam said, glaring.

Thomas' eyes moved to the collar of the dress's halter, where Rachel's rank insignia was displayed. "Of course. Pardon my breach of decorum, Captain. The Federated Commonwealth has a history of close-assault tactics. We can draw these Clans into our Wall of Steel and smash them up close, like we do with the Dracs and the Free Worlders."

Adam put his glass down and stared daggers at Hogarth. "General, respectfully, you never fought the Clans. I did, and I beat them. So learn this well: you cannot defeat them with standard 'Wall of Steel' tactics. Heroes at a hundred paces results in dead heroes we cannot afford."

Adam waved his hand and stormed off, Captain Specter behind him. "Well..." Thomas said. "History will show me right in the end."

And he picked up Adam's discarded drink and slammed it down.

HEARING AS TO THE SUITABILITY
OF THE HEAVY GAUSS RIFLE
1 OCTOBER 3059

Bench 1: And how long did it take for you to be proven right, General?

Hogarth: Our proof of concept was completed before the end of that year.

Bench 3: Is that what you call a quarter-ton maglev maintenance car being propelled on a rail by a VLAR 300 fusion engine?

Hogarth: I would like the record to show I loaned the reactor from my own *Atlas* for that test.

Bench 3: Yes, and a BattleMech that was already sold to a third party *and* your engine were both destroyed by what the supervising civilian technician called, and I quote, "an asinine experiment that proved nothing beyond the continued dominance of Ohm's Law."

FACTORY REFIT UNLOADING TRAINYARD
DEFIANCE INDUSTRIES TESTING ANNEX
FURILLO
FEDERATED COMMONWEALTH
20 DECEMBER 3055

Even with the target 'Mech 300 meters away, sparks were landing all around the jury-rigged control station. The result could only be described as an amputation of the *Valkyrie*'s torso, as the light 'Mech's legs and arms remained firmly clamped to the delivery gantry.

Thomas Hogarth was unable to control his excitement as he punched in the air! "*Jawohl!* Merry Christmas to all!"

A civilian engineer looked up from the fire extinguishers they were spraying on the smoking control panel. "Congratulations, General," the tech said. "You blew up two BattleMech engines to prove a choo-choo can move at Mach five."

"Thank you, lad!" Hogarth looked at the mix of fused power cabling and warped maglev rails that was supposed to be a test bench for a Gauss rifle. "Now when can we get this new Gauss rifle on my *Atlas*?"

The three techs looked at Thomas blankly. More sparks and flames shot up from the console, forcing the two with fire-suppression equipment to get back to work, leaving the third to answer.

He nervously cleared his throat. "Sir, this is not a Gauss rifle. It's...not even a *weapon*, per se. We made a simple mass driver out of train parts!"

"And got a quarter-ton slug to fire from it using a 'Mech engine. The only reason the engine is damaged is from lack of proper reinforcement." Hogarth stared at the smoldering console. "Isn't that just some tripped circuit breakers and whatnot?"

"Among other things," the lead tech said. "I should also point out that your test target was a brand-new BattleMech. "You noticed the black-and-red paint scheme? That was destined for the Kell Hounds. None of us are going to be responsible for that mess. You destroyed it."

"I did no such thing!" Hogarth retorted. "I didn't press any buttons! And besides, it is a Davion toy. Morgan Kell will thank me personally for relieving him of it."

HEARING AS TO THE SUITABILITY
   OF THE HEAVY GAUSS RIFLE
1 OCTOBER 3059

> **Hogarth:** So, yes, our proof-of-concept test did eventually bear fruit. We got nearly a dozen prototype weapons and conducted live-fire testing from fixed mounts.
> **Bench 1:** After five more years, correct?
> **Hogarth:** Innovation takes time and money, Your Honor.
> **Bench 2:** Your prototypes also missed several benchmarks outlined in the design documents, cartoons in the margins notwithstanding... According to documents, your most

promising heavy Gauss rifle is eighteen tons instead of the target sixteen. Effective range was reduced by nearly 100 meters. And the weapon had a chronic inability to maintain muzzle velocity beyond 200 meters.

Hogarth: Well, some compromises had to be made—

Bench 3: And then there is the issue of the uncontrollable recoil.

DEFIANCE FURILLO TESTING GROUNDS
FURILLO
LYRAN ALLIANCE
29 AUGUST 3059

"General," the test pilot from the Furillo Militia radioed, "my gyroscope is screaming at me. I am not sure the old girl can handle this." The MechWarrior was clearly nervous when not straining to keep his balance in the VTR-9K *Victor*.

"She will handle it, Leutnant," Hogarth replied on the radio. "Now begin the testing program." He was sitting on a lawn chair, a tankard of Kölsch on a table next to him. A thick cigar was wedged between his teeth while he looked out through a pair of digital binoculars.

The baby-blue-and-violet *Victor* sporting the prototype heavy Gauss rifle was leaning to its right side, the pilot clearly unable to compensate for the additional bulk of the weapon. The creaking of metal on metal as the casing grazed the 'Mech's thigh armor also spoke of poor actuator maintenance, a typical problem with nobility-owned machines that did not see regular service.

"We will begin with a static firing against a target representing a 65-ton *Loki* OmniMech." the rangemaster called over the radio. "Leutnant, you may fire when ready."

Hogarth pulled the binoculars up to his eyes and smiled. The Davion toy 'Mech needed to use its left arm to hold the massive new weapon steady. He was sure his own *Atlas* could do better. Still; he swore he would never lend his 'Mech for weapons testing again, not after an engineer convinced him to donate his 'Mech's engine.

"Range control, I am firing the weapon in three...two...one... Firing."

The heavy Gauss rifle *crack*ed a blue flash from the muzzle as electrical discharge and friction forced air to move out of the way of the projectile. The 'Mech-sized ferrocrete block that served as a target turned to powder under the impact of 250 kilograms of pure power driven at hypersonic speed.

"Leutnant, report!" a technician behind Hogarth called on the radio.

"No displays blew this time," the MechWarrior replied. "But my status indicators act like my actuators got hit by artillery. Arm's internal structure is also showing damage."

"General Hogarth," the tech said, "I recommend we suspend the test. If Hammerfist is already straining the *Victor*'s actuators—"

"Nonsense, son," Hogarth replied. "Actuator strain reflects real-world combat conditions. Commence with the mobile target."

"Sir, I really think—"

"Do what you are told!" Hogarth said as he picked up his tankard. "This is a controlled environment. Nothing can go wrong."

"Yes, sir." The technician pulled the mic close to his mouth. "Leutnant, the test will continue. Our next target is a simulated *Uller*. It will be moving at sixty-four kph and come within a hundred and twenty meters of your position. Target and fire at your leisure."

The *Victor* moved to its left side, the barrel of the heavy Gauss rifle slack at the hip, visible sparks flying from the BattleMech's shoulder. The ferrocrete pad that was the test's second target moved along its tracks, and the MechWarrior began drawing a bead on it.

"You got this, son," Hogarth said over the radio. "Nothing will go wrong."

A massive *crack* preceded an explosion from the BattleMech's right arm. The sheer force of the shot had formed a ditch in the ground, instantly vitrifying the soil along the path to the test target.

Hogarth leaped up and spouted a string of curses as the heavy Gauss rifle—and the *Victor*'s entire arm—landed ten meters from the observation tent, bouncing off the ferrocrete platform and over the tent. He followed the tumbling mount over his head and saw it land on his staff car, crushing it.

"What in the world happened?!" he shouted as the *Victor* fell on its back, motionless.

HEARING AS TO THE SUITABILITY
OF THE HEAVY GAUSS RIFLE
1 OCTOBER 3059

Bench 3: You later issued a court-martial summons to that test pilot in his hospital bed.

Hogarth: Of course I did! He destroyed LAAF property and put my life at risk.

Bench 2: And in your misguided zeal for justice, did it ever occur to you that that pilot was the son of the Duke of Summit? And that that *Victor* had been in their family since the days of

the Star League? The Estates General had to give the duke a lot of concessions to keep his hands from your throat. Since the duke's son received a medical discharge, the LAAF lost a MechWarrior from a notable dynasty. Not to mention the Requisitions Department had to replace the family's *Victor*.

Bench 1: He was only interested in being first on the waiting list for those new *BattleMaster*s because they are literally twice as expensive as the *Victor* you destroyed. So that makes four BattleMechs you have cost the LAAF due to the negligence in this endeavor.

Hogarth: Omelets and eggs, Your Honor. We learned much from that incident. Subsequent tests showed mounting the weapon in the torso prevents such catastrophic damage. I would stake my life on it.

Bench 2: Really? And how soon can we arrange such a test? [*Hogarth remains silent for several seconds.*]

Hogarth: Excuse me?

DEFIANCE FURILLO TESTING GROUNDS
FURILLO
LYRAN ALLIANCE
7 OCTOBER 3059

"I never should have staked my life on this!" Thomas Hogarth said as he approached his *Atlas*.

"General, we had to make accommodations," the lead tech explained. "Your short-range missile pods and ammunition were removed. And we installed some Cellular Ammunition Storage Equipment just beneath the Hammerfist, as a precaution."

Hogarth removed his custom-sewn royal-blue smoking jacket, revealing standard MechWarrior togs underneath. "And that will protect me from neurohelmet feedback if this goes wrong?"

"Oh, no, sir, your brain will still fry. The CASE will just keep your 'Mech intact and allow us to recover the Hammerfist prototype for further development."

Thomas put his hand on the technician's shoulder and smiled. "You're fired," he said, and hit the button on the scissor lift to ascend to his cockpit.

Minutes later, his *Atlas*, *Eisenbar*, was on the test field, and the heavy Gauss rifle's coils began charging.

"General Hogarth," the tech said over the radio, "your test begins. You will fire four rounds. Two at static targets, two at mobile targets.

As this is not a test of targeting proficiency, the mobile targets will move at thirty-two kilometers per hour."

Thomas exhaled in relief that that one accommodation was made.

He strode his *Atlas* into the designated place on the testing ground. His 'Mech's computer presented a blocky wireframe battlefield, and when the simulation completed rendering, two 'Mech-sized concrete blocks bore overlays of BattleMechs.

"General Hogarth," a sergeant in charge of data collection called over the radio, "you may commence when ready."

Hogarth walked his 'Mech at a leisurely pace to the middle of the testing area and gently drew a bead on the target whose overlay resembled a *Thor* OmniMech. As he pulled the trigger, he heard a loud hum throughout the cockpit before his 'Mech was rocked backward a step from the force of firing.

"*Scheiße!*" Hogarth called out, accidentally transmitting his shock to the very people judging him. Despite having not piloted his 'Mech for anything but pleasure cruises, Hogarth was able to maintain his balance, thrusting *Eisenbar*'s leg backward and planting it in the packed soil before he could completely lose his footing.

Not even waiting for the testing team, Hogarth walked the 'Mech more forcefully into position for the other stationary target. A simulated 60-ton *Galahad* bore down from an elevated position and fired as he broke the *Atlas* into a run. The Hammerfist's reticle came to rest over the center of the Clan sniper 'Mech, and Hogarth squeezed the trigger again.

The recoil brought *Eisenbar* to a dead stop while the nickel-ferrous slug pulverized the concrete target into debris.

"Very good, General. The moving targets will be next. Please maneuver to the starting point, and we will begin."

"*Ja, danke!*" Hogarth called out in his native German. "How is Hammerfist holding up?"

"We have some heat strain on the capacitors, but that is on the upper end of acceptable. Try not to fire it in such quick succession this time, and we should be good."

Hogarth steered his 'Mech to the designated test zone, and his targeting system painted icons over two more targets on rail cars: a *Valkyrie* and a *Javelin*.

"Someone knows I love smashing Davion toys," he muttered.

One target car made a serpentine motion across his line of fire, running west to east; the other was making a lateral push directly toward him from the rear of the arena. He could see just where the two targets were crossing and had an idea.

Opening up the 'Mech's throttle and firing his wrist-mounted medium lasers forced the faux *Javelin* to slow its advance on the track—just enough for the *Valkyrie* to catch up. Hogarth squeezed

Hammerfist's trigger, and the false *Valkyrie* shattered, its spalling concrete peppering the *Javelin* behind it. Despite the generous damage the shot caused, the *Javelin* kept moving toward Hogarth.

Before he could move out of the way, the target block rammed into *Eisenbar*'s knees. Caught completely off guard, the *Atlas* fell flat on its back without Hogarth so much as flailing the 'Mech's arms to keep balance. He was jostled around so much he did not realize he'd squeezed his primary trigger again, and the heavy Gauss rifle fired its fourth round as the fifteen-ton block of concrete was toppling over toward him.

But the force of the projectile caused the block to slide just enough so it only crushed the *Atlas'* forearm as it landed.

It took a few minutes for the ringing in his ears to cease. After slapping the quick release on his safety harness and undogging the cockpit hatch, Hogarth slumped against the side of his 'Mech. A faint buzzing in his neurohelmet radio grabbed his attention.

"General Hogarth, are you okay? Do you require assistance?"

"Fine, my boy, fine. Slipped on a roller skate is all. I presume the test failed?"

"Quite the opposite, General. You fired four test shots and hit four targets. Just barely clipped the last one before you fell. It registered as impacting right below the target's simulated neck joint."

"Well then. I need a staff car, a cold pint, and the lead tech to deliver a well-worded 'I told you so' to the investigative committee."

Silence from the radio told Hogarth something was amiss. "General...you fired the lead tech, just before the test began."

"Of course I did. Now tell him he is rehired! I have some gloating to do!"

A GAME OF ARMORED COMBAT: CELEBRATING 700 YEARS OF BATTLEMECH WARFARE

DANIEL ISBERNER

—*Gladiator Gazette*, March 3139

On 5 February of the thirty-ninth year of each century, the small and now-unimportant Terran town of Yakima becomes a hub for the rich and powerful as it hosts a celebration of the day the *Mackie*, the very first BattleMech, had its first combat trial. Nowadays, the *Mackie* itself has no value beyond what historians and collectors give it, but it is not really the *Mackie* itself that gets celebrated.

These centennial events commemorate 5 February 2439 as the birth of the BattleMech, the uncontested kings and queens of warfare, which brought a sudden and disruptive change to the battlefield. Every 100 years, the mayor of Yakima invites the Great House leaders and several other important personages of the Inner Sphere to celebrate. But 3139 was different. With Terra being cut off behind the Wall, Defiance Industries, the best-known manufacturer of BattleMechs in the Lyran Commonwealth, decided to host this century's festivities at their facilities on Furillo instead, which resulted in one of the most expensive publicity stunts in recent history.

While not every head of state can attend these events, each celebration always attracts a high-profile crowd around. This year, however, no House lords made an appearance. Even Melissa Steiner, Archon of the Lyran Commonwealth, was officially excused from attendance because she is preoccupied with the ongoing conflict with former-Free Worlds League provinces. Security concerns during a Defiance Industries event might have been the unofficial reason, though.

Nevertheless, a surprising number of CEOs from military manufacturers attended, including representatives from Clan Sea Fox. Most of the attendees seemed disappointed to miss the chance to pitch their newest and most expensive hardware directly to foreign rulers, but each nation's emissaries were still around to strike deals in backrooms during the ball.

All of that was just the precursor to the actual event, however. This century, Defiance Industries had something special prepared to distract from the fact that the celebration was not happening on Terra.

When the first part of the big ball was over, the crowd was invited outside to watch an undisclosed but advertised "special event of stellar proportions."

Once outside, the CFO of Defiance Industries, George Dyson, announced we would now watch a never-before-seen duel.

Six BattleMechs faced each other on a prepared battlefield. Five hand-built versions of the original MSK-5S *Mackie* prototypes against a single new *Atlas II* model, Defiance's AS7-DK-H.

Even with five-against-one odds, the winner seemed already predestined, because the original MSK-5S model was still built on a heavier and less-powerful primitive tech base compared to the modern *Atlas II*. But the crowd still gasped once the next surprise was revealed: the *Atlas II* would be piloted by Manfred Cunningham, a direct descendent of Colonel Charles Kincaid, the very first MechWarrior. The betting on the battle instantly changed because Cunningham was not a trained MechWarrior.

(Check out our full interview with George Dyson and Manfred Cunningham on page 17.)

Did Defiance rig the battle? There is evidence that the original battle on Terra was rigged, so given the outcome of this one, we can assume the same thing happened again. Still, the fight was a good show. Using training ammo and powered-down lasers, the six 'Mechs started firing at each other, maneuvering around the proving ground, and exchanging blow after blow until there was only one clear victor: the AS7-DK-H *Atlas II*.

After the fight, everyone went back inside, and Manfred Cunningham eventually joined the crowd. While he looked clean and shaved, it was clear this man was no warrior. After speaking with him for only a few minutes, it was even more obvious he had spent his entire life not knowing who his ancestors were. Did he realize he was just there to be shown off as Defiance Industries' special pet? It didn't seem like it, but you, dear reader, will have to read our interview and decide for yourself.

The few warriors in the crowd kept their distance, which was a clear sign they had also noticed Cunningham was not a real MechWarrior. None of that stopped the dignitaries in the group from almost crushing him between them, however. They showered the man with questions just so they could claim to have met a descendant of Charles Kincaid and shaken his hand. It was an odd sight.

After the dignitaries were done with Cunningham, almost all of them went into the backrooms to hammer out some deals with Defiance Industries salespeople, so the mock duel did indeed help grease some wheels. Based on the ever-increasing smiles from the Defiance reps on the floor, it's fair to assume that quite a few orders for their new *Atlas II* were placed before the festivities concluded.

As the party went on and more and more people left, a very drunk Manfred Cunningham was quietly ushered out by Defiance personnel. And with the big surprise of the evening gone, everyone else left too.

THE GRACELAND GAFFE
A MECHWARRIOR: DESTINY MISSION BRIEFING

CHRIS HUSSEY

REGATON WILDLANDS
GRACELAND
LYRAN ALLIANCE
5 FEBRUARY 3058

Tharkan Media Associates is one of the biggest media conglomerates in the Lyran Alliance. Since the halt of the Clans on Tukayyid, TMA has been beyond busy producing numerous holovid series and feature films. The current trend in entertainment is anything involving Inner Sphere militaries overcoming the ever-present threat of the Clans. While the House militaries may be keenly aware of who and what the Clans are, the general populace still has a healthy amount of fear of these invaders, especially in the Alliance.

Their next big series is called *The Filthy Lucy*. It tells the dramatic tales of a mercenary unit of the same name stationed along the Lyran/Falcon/Viper border. The team has been hired to act as both extras and advisors for some of the 'Mech-combat scenes in this series.

COMMANDER'S CALL
PITCH MEETING

"You gotta be kidding me!"

Burgess shook his head. "Nope. We got him!" He lifted a sweaty hand, stained with taco sauce, for a high five from his production partner, Nick. The gesture was met with enthusiasm and a few flying shreds of lettuce.

"You're telling me Rufus Cameron, the hottest director in the Alliance, is gonna direct half the episodes in our first season?"

Burgess took another bite of his taco. "He had a few stipulations, though."

Nick nodded. Burgess' pause telegraphed that Nick might not like what was coming next. "Such as?"

Burgess swallowed. "You know how big he is on realism. Using practical effects and all that. He wants all his stuff filmed with live 'Mechs and simulated weapons. Minimal CGI."

Nick blanched. "Does he have any idea how expensive that is?"

Burgess waved off his concern. "We'll make it up on the backend with his name alone. Hire some low-rent mercs to cut costs. I've already got scouts hunting for shooting locations." He took another bite, then sent a small, playful jab into Nick's shoulder. "C'mon, buddy. You handle the bean counters, and I'll handle the divas. This is our big break!"

Nick shoveled a handful of chips in his mouth and washed them down with a swig of beer. "You better be right."

Players will earn 4 XP for completing this mission.

OBJECTIVES

- Choreograph a fake engagement between the characters' unit and the actors.
- Drive off the Steel Viper force while keeping the cast and crew safe.
- Once the dust has settled, the show must go on, but the direction is left up to the team.

CUES

- We need to make this look dramatic. Realism is secondary.
- This needs to look as real as possible.
- Does this curved cockpit glass make me look fat? My "good side" is not "inside" that 'Mech.
- Are those real Steel Vipers? Who hired real Steel Vipers?!
- Forget about them; they're non-union crew and extras. Save me!
- That footage wasn't in your contract, so we don't feel obligated to pay extra for it. Don't ComStar us, we'll ComStar you.

TAGS

- Lyran Alliance
- Steel Vipers
- Acting

- Movie Extras
- The Show Must Go On

SETTING

Graceland is a temperate world with a wide variety of terrain, climates, and seasons, making it ideal for the production of *The Filthy Lucy*. The planet's population and defenses are clustered together in and around the population centers, allowing the production crew to shoot in rural or sparsely populated locations. This is a double-edged sword, as it gives the cast and crew privacy, but also makes them the center of attention in the small town of Regaton, located nearby.

The planet is also under the threat from Clan Steel Viper, which is only one jump away.

SCENES

Scene 1: *Suggested NPCs: cast and director (Media Celebrity), stunt coordinators (MechWarrior), effects technicians (Technician)*

The team is hired to help choreograph a battle scene and acting as the opposition in this fight. Their 'Mechs are outfitted with various fake add-ons, making them look more sinister and alien, as they will be playing members of Clan Malachite Osprey, a purposely bad-sounding Clan name.

The cast members have a wide range of personality types. Lead actress Ella MacLeod (Lucy) proves especially difficult. On the opposite end, cast member Augustin Hache (Templeton) is quite earnest and interested in the characters and their lives. Chester Grimes (Lewis) and Cosette Moreau (Two-Guns Terri) lie somewhere in between.

Director Rufus Cameron wants a spectacular scene, but because of his love of realism, he's open to the idea of the team's expertise. Director of Photography Casey Heger only wants the "sexiest" shots and often suggests things contrary to the team's ideas. It's very possible some team members might even get a few lines!

All the 'Mechs are outfitted with explosive effects charges, powered-down lasers, and dummy autocannon rounds for the scenes.

The fight must also showcase the special weapon wielded by Lucy, the 'Mech flail.

Acting, Negotiation, Piloting (BattleMech), Tactics, and even *Demolitions* are skills that could play a part in this scene.

Scene 2: *Suggested NPCs: cast (Media Celebrity), Steel Viper attack Star (MechWarrior), various townsfolk (Reporter)*

Weeks ago, a member of the Steel Viper Watch reported on the "mysterious tech" of the crew (the 'Mech flail), and now a Steel Viper attack force is about to crash the production. Star Captain Hollis' *batchall* was answered by the production crew, who didn't know any better.

The Vipers are focused on acquiring the flail from Ella's 'Mech. Depending on how the battle was staged, the team could find itself fighting in the town of Regaton, or in the wildlands outside of town. Regardless, most of the cast in the fight have little to no military experience, but they are still piloting 'Mechs. The team also needs to overcome their stage weaponry (including the insurance-mandated safety locks on their energy weapons), guide the cast and crew to safety, or rally them in the fight against the Vipers.

Plot Points can be used to grant easier access to the team's real ammo stores or other advantages to slow the Vipers down. The battle can end with the Vipers being driven off, or possibly even escaping with the 'Mech flail, and possibly even with Ella.

Scene 3: *Suggested NPCs: Talent agents (Courtesan), lawyers (House Liaison), Lyran intelligence agents*

With the battle over, the story can proceed in all manner of directions. Was it a clear victory? The actual battleROM footage could be worth a lot to the production crew. Was Ella taken captive? The story may now take a plot twist into a rescue mission. The appearance of the 'Mech flail and the Viper attack may also draw the attention of Lyran intelligence.

MAKING THEM PAY: MERCENARY LOGISTICS AND FINANCES FOR THE FREEBOOTING QUARTERMASTER

STEPHEN TOROPOV

—By Stephani Ehli, MercStar Press, Galatea, 3151. Excerpt from first chapter.

The mercenary trade is a two-pronged business. Success on the battlefield brings notoriety and clout, but even units with Sphere-wide name recognition must ensure that their deployments actually turn a profit. This profit imperative may result in business decisions that appear cutthroat, but a bleeding heart will kill a mercenary company as dead as a Gauss slug, and the logistical decisions of the accountants and quartermasters often make the difference. Arranging transport, securing supplies, and cultivating reliable local partners will bring a company closer to victory without a shot being fired.

A constant bugbear for small- and medium-sized mercenary companies is the need for transportation to the site of a contract. It is all too easy for a large sign-on bonus to tempt a commander into accepting a mission, only to discover the destination planet is ten Kearny-Fuchida jumps away, and far from standard JumpShip trade routes. They can then only watch in dismay as the unit's entire up-front payment disappears into chartering the necessary docking collars. The farther-flung a contract is, the more important it is for a command's negotiators to insist the employer cover as much of the transit cost as possible. It is also vital to scope out additional employment opportunities near the site of a long-distance deployment. This may often involve taking follow-on jobs with forces you fought against in the initial contract, but as long as your employer's money still spends, the margins on such local missions are significantly higher than missions that require a return trip to a hiring hall. Turning your coat often turns a profit.

Despite the financial heartache of chartering JumpShip collars and even DropShip berths to reach a contract, a growing command should be careful to moderate the urge to purchase its own transportation assets too quickly. Owning and operating aerospace transportation alleviates some acute transportation costs, but now the unit must directly bankroll the crew salaries, consumable costs, customs fees, and DropPort pad rents that charter space captains charge their premiums to cover. In addition, a newly purchased DropShip is a major capital asset that many opponents will view as a valid military target, so its defense must be figured into each deployment plan. Too many promising mercenary units rush for the status symbol of owning their own DropShip, only to drown in the heady mixture of debt, operating costs, and buyer's remorse. Avoid making the leap to owning JumpShip assets until the unit's financial portfolio has enough credit and liquid assets to absorb both the purchase price and several deployments' worth of operation costs. Until that standard can be met, it is financially advisable for a command to instead focus on negotiating for prospective employers to provide either direct transportation or generous reimbursement of travel costs as part of a contract.

On the other hand, it is often preferable for a mercenary unit to negotiate away direct logistical support from their employer. A BattleMech will consume significant supplies of ammunition and spare armor plating even on a quiet garrison contract. A nimble quartermaster can often find better deals on such supplies than the local militia's logistics officers can, and over time a command can build up strong relationships with regional suppliers that would be out of reach if the unit is contractually obligated to buy from the "company store." When doing such comparison shopping, discretion is often paramount, as retailers who sell military materiel at cut-rate prices often procure their stock from sources responsible employers might take issue with. In such circumstances, remember that you shouldn't ask questions you (or your employer) don't want answers to. Suppliers appreciate customers who show discretion, and they can move proverbial mountains for such partners.

Cultivating loyal business relationships with suppliers for logistical goods and services is never a bad idea. Not only can it lead to valuable discounts and exclusive deals, but suppliers also often have very relevant political and economic leverage. Local militaries need good arms merchants as much or more than mercenaries do, particularly on worlds with no native military-manufacturing facilities. Coincidentally, such worlds frequently hire mercenaries for garrison work, since they lack assets a national military deems worthy of permanent defense. Bringing up friendly connections to viable gunrunners can sweeten the deal for backwater employers, and threatening to turn that tap off can be a useful bit of leverage in dispute should they try to waver or welsh.

Perhaps the most important—and certainly the most overlooked—logistical relationship a mercenary company relies on is with the manual laborers who physically handle supplies and maintenance. The precise name and organization of these laborers often changes from planet to planet; they may be a longshoreman's union, astech association, stevedore's guild, labor corporation, or the service staff of a local noble. However they are organized, no serious military organization can afford to ignore the essential service they provide in efficiently packing, organizing, and delivering military supplies, especially as they often also form the labor pool temporary military astechs are pulled from. Making a dedicated effort to understand and accommodate these labor organizations will often earn you a major local ally, and one used to being taken for granted by their planetary society. Even the most imperious employer cannot realistically threaten to terminate a mercenary unit's contract and just hire a new unit if the local labor organization is willing to grind all military operations to a halt in support of their sellsword friends and defenders. Across the entire Inner Sphere, you'll find no other group more willing to help make the boss pay.

THREE WHITE ROSES

CRAIG A. REED, JR.

OURAY
SEKULMUN
CAPELLAN MARCH
FEDERATED SUNS
29 APRIL 2525

From a window on the top floor of the palace's west wing, Cadmon watched the city, the traffic flow, and the movement of the pedestrians below. Night had fallen, but the palace's surroundings were brightly lit compared to the city beyond the palace walls. In the distance, he could see the lights of the spaceport.

He wore a Federated Peacekeeping Forces infantry uniform, fabric cap, comm gauntlets, and field boots. A narrow white band on his epaulets marked him as a captain, and the red background of the epaulets also declared him a MechWarrior. The modified Federated Suns shoulder patch—the sword over a sunburst had a crown added above the sword—marked him as one of the First Prince's bodyguards. A small message case was on his left hip, a pistol on his right.

He glanced around. The hall was void of any cover, and the few doors in sight were all locked, checked every hour by a roving security patrol. The west wing was the palace's high-security section, where ballistic glass and reinforced walls were designed to withstand an assault.

Cadmon resisted the urge to look at his watch, knowing he was being observed by the security cameras around the hall. He was a Federated Peacekeeping Forces officer, not a raw recruit, and he wasn't about to give Prince David Varnay any satisfaction by showing agitation.

Cadmon didn't like the man. The Prince of the Capellan March was someone he didn't trust, even if he was a regent for the now seventeen-year-old First Prince Alexander Davion. In his role as commander of Alexander's personal bodyguard detail, Cadmon didn't trust anyone, but even if his private orders from his commanding officer, General Philippine Cantrick—which boiled down to "Don't trust Varnay as far as you can throw him, and that includes throwing him off a cliff"—had been any different, Cadmon still would not have trusted Varnay.

Just then, he heard footsteps, and turned slowly as Varnay and his bodyguards came into view. Behind them followed a man with a shaved head and dressed in dark clothing. As they approached, Cadmon snapped to attention and saluted.

"At ease, Captain," Varnay said with a flip of his hand instead of a return salute. He was one of the regents ruling the Federated Suns, along with Alexander's aunts—Laura Davion and Varnay's wife, Cassandra Davion—and General Nikoli Rostov. For most of the past twelve years, the regents had ruled while also maneuvering to claim the throne for themselves. Varnay and Cassandra had outmaneuvered Laura and Rostov, spiriting away the young First Prince and marrying him to Varnay's niece, Cynthia. Now that Alexander was on a "tour" of the Capellan March, the Varnays were keeping him away from Laura and Rostov and a now-pregnant Cynthia. It didn't take a genius to see what was going on: once Alexander's heir was born, he would no longer be needed.

Cadmon shifted to an at-ease stance. "Yes, my Lord Regent."

"Who's this?" the man with the shaved head asked.

Cadmon's stomach tightened, and he gave the speaker a long, measuring gaze. A pair of flat gray eyes returned his look, and a slight pull of a smile appeared in one corner of the man's mouth.

"I could ask the same thing of you," Cadmon said in a steady voice.

Varnay looked at Cadmon for a few seconds, then at the bald man. "You two haven't met, have you?"

"Don't believe we have," Varnay's associate said.

"Captain Mallory, this is Mr. Ferryman, a special security consultant in my employ. Ferryman, this is Captain Cadmon Mallory, commander of Prince Alexander's personal protection detail."

Varnay hadn't counted on one thing when he took Alexander away from New Avalon: the Royal Brigade of the Federated Peacekeeping Forces. Cadmon and a platoon of soldiers had been sent to guard the First Prince, and despite everything Varnay tried, they had done their job for the last two years. Fortunately, the regulations and force of law gave Cadmon the upper hand in this, despite Varnay's bluster and threats. Now, Cadmon and two squads guarded the First Prince, while the rest of the platoon were on New Syrtis, guarding Cynthia and her unborn child.

Ferryman's eyes narrowed, and his gaze shifted to a more guarded expression. "That must be a fun job," he said, injecting sarcasm into his words. "Trailing around after some snot-nosed kid barely out of diapers, making sure he isn't taking advantage of the maids."

Cadmon let the insult wash over him, counted to ten, then smiled. "Protecting the First Prince is a great honor and responsibility."

Varnay coughed. "I wish to speak to Captain Mallory alone."

Ferryman nodded and motioned to the bodyguards. All of them walked away, but stopped after a short distance, leaving Varnay and Cadmon in a bubble of space.

The regent reminded Cadmon of a librarian he'd met as a teenager. Varnay was shorter than him by a dozen centimeters, thin, with a narrow face and nose. He wore a dark suit, with a high collar and the sun-and-sword pin on the lapel. He had a relaxed expression on his face, but Cadmon noticed the tightness around his eyes and in his neck and shoulders. "You have the messages?"

"Yes, my lord." Cadmon held up the small case.

"Good. Give them to me."

Cadmon frowned. "All of them?"

Varnay fixed the captain with a stare, his muddy brown eyes narrowing dangerously. "Was I unclear?"

"No, my lord." Cadmon opened the case and extracted several discs, which he handed over.

The regent took the discs and nodded. "Alexander will receive these in the morning. You are dismissed, Captain."

Cadmon came to attention again, but Varnay was already walking away. By the time he'd taken his fourth step, the bodyguards had surrounded him, with Ferryman trailing after them. As they turned down a side corridor, Ferryman stopped, turned, and looked at Cadmon one last time, then followed the others.

Cadmon silently counted to 100, then went in the opposite direction.

The soldiers on guard in front of the First Prince's suite straightened when Cadmon came into their view. One of them, a sergeant, stepped forward and snapped off a precise salute.

Cadmon returned the salute and nodded at the other three, smiling slightly. "Quiet night, Sacco?"

"So far, sir," Sergeant Sacco replied. He was a fireplug of a man, as tall as Regent Varnay, but more muscular.

Cadmon tapped the message case. "I have the First Prince's itinerary for tomorrow. Is he still awake?"

"As far as I know, sir," Sacco replied. "You know what he's like the first few nights on a new planet." He turned to look at one of the other guards. "Deats, knock on the door and let Bambridge know Captain Mallory's here."

The lanky corporal rapped on the door three times, paused, and knocked twice more. Twenty seconds passed before the door opened and Bambridge, the First Prince's valet, looked out and nodded to Cadmon.

"Captain Mallory," he said, his voice warm and rich. "The First Prince is waiting." He stepped back and opened the door wide enough to allow Cadmon into the suite.

Beyond the door, the hall was luxuriously furnished—garishly so, in Cadmon's opinion. The scarlet-and-gold carpet felt spongy under his boots, and the walls were painted a deep red with gold trimmings. Several paintings, each one depicting a past Davion Prince, hung on the walls, their presence a reminder of whose suite this was.

A soft cough reminded Cadmon of Bambridge's presence. He turned toward the servant, removed his cap, and handed it to him. Bambridge murmured his thanks and placed the cap on a side table with legs so thin Cadmon thought it would collapse at any moment.

"The Prince is in the library, sir," Bambridge said as they began walking down the hall. "Would you like some tea?"

"Please," Cadmon replied. "What's his mood?"

"He's on edge, sir, as any expectant father would be."

"He isn't the only one. Regent Varnay's the same."

"The Lady Cynthia is his niece. It would be reasonable for him to be expectant."

Cadmon sighed. "Aye, but I think he's too eager."

They reached a white door. Bambridge knocked twice, paused, then three more times before opening the door. "If you will excuse me, I'll get the tea."

The library was large, and except for two doors, the walls were entirely lined with floor-to-ceiling bookcases. Roomy, comfortable-looking chairs were scattered around, and in one near the center of the room, a young man sat. He looked up when Cadmon entered, put down the book he was reading, and smiled. "Cad!" he said, standing quickly.

Cadmon nodded to him. "My Prince."

Prince Alexander Simon Lucian Davion was not yet eighteen, but looked a couple of years younger. He had short, dark hair, striking features, and light blue eyes. He wore a bathrobe over silk pajamas and slippers. "The itinerary?" he said, eyeing the case.

"Among other things. Room been scanned?"

Alexander sighed. "Twice. First by Sergeant Sacco and his team, then by Bambridge and myself. We're clean."

"Good. Can't be too careful, my Prince. We're on Varnay's turf, and we have few allies. The more we can keep him in the dark, the better."

Alexander nodded. "I know." He stood and rubbed his hands together. He was slightly shorter than Cadmon, with a swimmer's build. "What do we have tonight?"

"The usual," Cadmon replied, reaching inside his dress jacket. "Varnay has the original dispatches, but here's the copies and the *real* message from Lady Cynthia." He pulled out several discs and handed them to Alexander. "They're all marked."

The Prince took the discs and smiled. "Thank you, Cad."

"It's my duty, my Prince."

The second door opened and Bambridge entered, carrying a tray. "Tea, sire."

Alexander motioned to a side table with a flick of his hand, his attention now on the discs. He pulled one out and went over to the table next to his chair. He picked up a noteputer, slid the disc into the slot for it, and stared at the screen. Cadmon could hear an indistinct feminine voice coming from the noteputer's speaker. He walked to the corner of the room where Bambridge had placed the tray.

The valet looked at Alexander, then at Cadmon. "Lady Cynthia?"

"Aye."

Bambridge nodded and poured a cup of tea. Cadmon took the cup, added cream and sweetener, and watched Alexander stare at the noteputer screen. The young Prince's expression was wonder mixed with wistfulness as his wife brought him up to date on her and the soon-to-be-born baby's condition.

Varnay had not taken into account that his niece and Alexander would fall deeply in love with each other. Instead of being her uncle's tool, Cynthia Varnay had become Alexander's closest and strongest ally. Despite being on New Syrtis, she remained in close contact with Alexander, going so far as to record two different messages—one which would be seen by her uncle, the other by Alexander alone. It was a dangerous game, but Cadmon was willing to help the couple any way he could, going so far as to personally pick up the messages from the planet's Federated Peacekeeping Forces communications center.

After several minutes, Alexander stopped the recording, grabbed a paper and a pen from the table next to him, and started the recording again. He scribbled on the sheet, then folded it and placed it on the table. After several more minutes, he turned the noteputer off, ejected the disc, and placed it in the pocket of his bathrobe. He closed his eyes for a few seconds, then opened them. He looked at Cadmon. "Thank you."

"It's my duty, my Prince."

"Still, thank you." He stopped, then said, "Cad, have you ever been in love?"

"Never had the time."

"You should make the time. Love changes you, makes you a different person."

"If you say so, my Prince. Right now, the sole duty of me and my team is to protect you from anyone wishing to do you harm."

"Including Uncle David?"

Cadmon smiled thinly. "*Especially* Regent Varnay."

Alexander returned the smile. Well, let's see if we can frustrate him a bit." He picked up the paper and held it out to Cadmon. "Cynthia came through with a way to contact the anti-Varnay resistance on-planet. The leaders of the local resistance forces call themselves Justinian and Theodora."

Cadmon took the paper. "I'll take care of it, my Prince."

OURAY CITY
SEKULMUN
CAPELLAN MARCH
FEDERATED SUNS
2 MAY 2525

The bar was located near the spaceport, the patrons mostly DropShip crew and cargo handlers. The neon sign outside the bar read ZAHARA'S, but time and neglect had blacked out a few letters, leaving only HAR 'S showing in the darkness. A few older vehicles were parked on the street.

"Don't like it," Sacco muttered.

"Don't have to like it," Cadmon replied. "Just watch my back."

The pair were standing in a dark alley across from the bar. This part of Ouray wasn't as well-lit as the area around the duke's palace, as the working streetlights were few and far between. At this time of night, the streets were nearly deserted, and the sounds of the city were few and muffled, occasionally overwhelmed by the sounds of an arriving or departing DropShip.

"Think the duke's guards will miss us tonight?"

Cadmon smiled tightly at his sergeant. "After this, I intend on making a surprise inspection of palace's security. We don't need Kalvin Liao's assassins doing Varnay's work for him." He glanced at his watch. "Let's go."

The two stepped onto the street and approached the bar. Cadmon in front, Sacco behind and to his left. They were dressed in the type of rough clothing worn by cargo handlers and DropShip crewmen. Both carried pistols, but only in case of trouble.

The bar had the look that reflected its patrons—rough, hard, and well-used. When they entered, Cadmon felt every eye on him and Sacco, and the babble of conversations faltered. Ignoring the patrons, Cadmon walked toward the bar, Sacco behind him. He nodded to the bartender, who glowered at them.

"Two beers," Cadmon said, taking a gold coin from his pocket. He placed it on the top of the bar, but held his hand over it.

The barkeep's expression became guarded. "Haven't seen you around here before."

"We're from New Avalon, via New Syrtis. Got in late last night and worked like dogs until just now."

"Sounds rough."

Cadmon nodded. "Tell me about it!" He removed the hand from the coin, revealing the profile of Simon Davion on the obverse.

The bartender raised an eyebrow, but took the coin to the cash register. He returned and handed over the change. As Cadmon's hand closed around the coins, he felt something that wasn't a coin. He pocketed the change, took the beers, then noticed an empty table in the back of the room next to a hallway leading to the bathrooms. He gave Sacco a beer, then headed to the table.

By the time they reached the table, the conversation was at its normal levels, and both men sat down. "Now what?" Sacco muttered, sipping his beer.

Cadmon surreptitiously scanned the room as he reached into his pocket and fished around for the non-coin from the bartender. Keeping his hand below the table, he drew out the item and saw a piece of paper folded so it was the same size as the coins. He opened the note one-handed and read the message:

Go down hallway, turn right, door at end of hall. Knock twice, count to five, two more knocks.

Cadmon glanced at his watch. "Hallway," he said, refolding the note and putting it back into his pocket. The two rose from the table, leaving their beers behind.

The hallway was poorly lit, its badly painted walls peeling and with noticeable cracks. At the other end, the lefthand branch led to the restrooms, and the longer hall to the right ended in a single door.

Cadmon turned right, Sacco following. At the door, Cadmon knocked twice, counted to five, then knocked twice more. He waited another five-count, then tried the handle. The door opened smoothly, but beyond lay darkness.

"Come in," said a female voice from within, "and keep your hands where we can see them."

Both soldiers walked in. Cadmon heard the door close behind him, then banks of lights snapped on, illuminating the room.

Shielding his eyes, he glanced around the square cinder-block storeroom. Work lights mounted on stands at the far end of the room were directed at the door. Bottles and crates on shelves lined the walls.

A figure outlined by the light sat in a chair. "No sudden movements," the same voice said, "or you will be shot."

"Hello to you too," Cadmon said.

"What's the password?" The voice was mature, with a clipped tone.

"Three white roses."

"Representing?"

"Alexander, Cynthia, and Vincent. Countersign?"

"The precepts of the law are these: to live honestly, to injure no one, and give everyone their due."

There was silence, then all but one of the work lights went out, dimming the room to a twilight level. The figure rose and approached them. "At ease, boys," she said. "They're friends."

Cadmon heard movement behind him, but didn't look back. Instead, he looked at the woman. "You're Theodora."

"You've heard of me," the woman replied.

"Part of my job. You and Justinian top the list of the Capellan March's most-wanted terrorists."

"Terrorists?" Theodora's face remained in shadow because of the light behind her and how her dark hair hung around her face. She chuckled. "Anyone who opposes Varnay is a terrorist in his eyes."

"If you say so. I don't know anything about you except someone important vouches for you."

"You're against Varnay?"

"Aye," Cadmon replied, "Where's Justinian?"

"Around," Theodora replied. "Is it true the First Prince is a spoiled brat who has three mistresses with him?"

Cadmon snorted. "Prince Alexander's no more a spoiled brat than Kalvin Liao is a sane and stable Chancellor. He loves one woman—his wife and soon-to-be mother of his son, Lady Cynthia."

Theodora was silent for a few moments. "All right," she said. "That matches up with what we know. What do you want from us?"

"Passage off-planet and out of the system, away from the Confederation border."

"How many and what luggage?"

"No more than twenty passengers, light luggage."

"When?"

"Well, that's the tricky part..."

OURAY CITY
SEKULMUN
CAPELLAN MARCH
FEDERATED SUNS
5 MAY 2525

An air of expectation hung over the duke's palace. Everyone, from Regent Varnay down to the lowest palace servant, was waiting for the news of the heir's birth. The regent was on edge, staring out the window every time a DropShip landed at the spaceport. Alexander, when he wasn't in public, paced his suite like a caged tiger.

Cadmon funneled his energy into staying on top of the palace's security. As the on-site commander of Alexander's protection detail, his authority exceeded his rank by several magnitudes. Alexander's security came first; everything else came second.

Cadmon's plan to get the Prince off-planet was also underway. The day after his meeting with Theodora, Varnay had informed Cadmon that the First Prince was staying on Sekulmun for an extra week. Cadmon had merely said, "Very good, my lord," and continued planning the Prince's escape.

Cadmon was in his office, a cubicle barely large enough to hold a desk and two chairs, when there was a knock at the door. "Enter."

Sacco stuck his head in. "Sir," he said. "The Regent wishes to see the Prince at once. He says he has important news."

"How important?"

"The press flacks are excitedly running around, and Varnay looks pleased." The sergeant glanced back into the hall, then looked at Cadmon. "Ferryman's with him."

Cadmon heart beat faster. He stood. "Activate Rosebud Two. If it's the news we're expecting, we execute."

"Yes, sir."

There were eight men in the group. Varnay, his bodyguards, and Ferryman were in front, with Cadmon and Sacco two steps behind. Cadmon felt uneasy, as Varnay's expression was more pleased than happy. On the other hand, Cadmon had resisted the urge to wipe the smirk off Ferryman's face with a good overhand right.

His fears grew when they entered the hallway leading to the suite. The four guards on duty weren't his troops. Instead, they wore midnight-blue uniforms with peaked caps and held submachine guns.

Cadmon scowled. "What's going on here? Where are my people?"

Varnay said, "These guards are here on my orders, Captain."

Cadmon glared at the regent. "My lord, I must protest! My troops—"

"—need a break," Varnay said. "You and your people have been on duty for two years without pause. But tonight, they can celebrate." He motioned to Ferryman. "Mr. Ferryman's team is very good at their job."

Cadmon glare shifted to Ferryman. "The Prince's safety is *my* concern!"

"Relax, soldier boy," Ferryman said, his smirk becoming a grin. "We can look after the boy for a night."

"That 'boy' is the First Prince of the Federated Suns!" Cadmon shouted. "Not some disaffected teenager trying to stay up past his bedtime!"

"Captain!" Varnay snarled.

Cadmon came to attention. "Sir!"

"The matter is settled. You and your troops have the night off. Is that clear?"

"Lord Regent, I strongly protest those orders!"

"So noted." Varnay nodded to one of the guards, who banged on the door.

Bambridge answered the door. The servant's expression was neutral, but from the slight stiffness in his stance, Cadmon also knew he was angry. "The Prince will see you," he said, stepping back and opening the door wider.

If Varnay noticed Bambridge's displeasure, he didn't care. He strolled into the suite, Ferryman following. "Where is the Prince?"

"The library, my lord," Bambridge replied. "Would you like some tea?"

Varnay waved his hand. "Tea? This is a time for *celebration*! Champagne, if you have it, good liquor if you don't!"

"I'll see what we have, my lord. If you will please follow me."

Cadmon leaned in close to Sacco. "Stay here," he whispered. "Pass the word to the detail: Alert Level Orange."

"Right," Sacco muttered.

Cadmon followed Varnay and Ferryman into the library. Alexander was sprawled on a couch, reading a book. He was still wearing his dress uniform from the morning's inspection tour, though the collar was open and the jacket's clasps were mostly undone. His boots and half a dozen books were scattered around him in a haphazard fashion. He glanced up when Varnay coughed politely, then dropped the book when he saw the trio and sat up. "Oh, Uncle!"

Cadmon noticed a flicker of annoyance cross Varnay's face, but it vanished quickly. He smiled. "My Prince! I have good news! You're a father!"

Alexander sprang to his feet. "When?" he asked excitedly. "Is Cynthia all right? Is the baby?"

Varnay grinned. "Both mother and son are doing well. Congratulations, my Prince. You have an heir."

Alexander grinned back. "Wonderful! Do you have any pictures?"

Cadmon's eyes scanned the library. In one corner, he noticed a vase with three white roses in it. His eyes narrowed. Three white roses was a signal telling Alexander he had a son and heir. They had not been here earlier in the day, when Cadmon had stopped by to collect Alexander for a meeting with the local military commanders.

"Of course, my Prince," Varnay replied, handing Alexander a disc. "There's also a personal message on this from Cynthia."

Alexander turned and searched for his noteputer. Once he found it, Bambridge entered the library with a tray of glasses and a bottle. "The only champagne we have on hand is a bottle of 2487 Le Harve, my lord," he said.

"It'll have to do," Varnay said, waving the servant over to him. "Captain Mallory, Mr. Ferryman, will you join me in a toast to the First Prince's son and heir?"

"Any reason to drink is a good one," Ferryman said eagerly. "What about you, soldier boy?"

Cadmon wanted to refuse, but as he looked over at Alexander, he caught his Prince looking at him and gave him a slight nod. "I'll have a small glass."

Varnay picked up the bottle and gave it a few shakes. "My Prince, please join us."

"In a moment," Alexander said. He was sitting on the couch again, hunched over the noteputer. Cadmon could hear a feminine voice coming from the noteputer, and the Prince was staring intently at the screen.

A sudden *pop* made Cadmon's head snap in the direction of the sound as the champagne flowed out of the bottle and spilled into several of the glasses and onto the tray. Varnay poured four glasses, and handed one to Ferryman.

Cadmon immediately stepped forward and took the other two glasses, then held one of them out to Alexander. "My Prince?"

Alexander looked up, and Cadmon could see tears in the young man's eyes. "I should have been there," he said softly. "I should have been there for my son's birth."

"You are a Prince of the Federated Suns," Cadmon said. "Sometimes, duty takes precedence over family matters."

"I know," Alexander said, taking the glass from his hand. "But I still should have been there."

"As soon as we finish the tour, my Prince," Varnay said. "But now, a toast, to the First Prince and his new heir!"

"To the First Prince and his new heir!" both Ferryman and Cadmon said, raising their glasses, Ferryman's smirk raising Cadmon's hackles.

Cadmon took a sip of the champagne and looked back at Alexander. The Prince, still holding his untouched glass, was staring back at the noteputer's screen. Suddenly, he tapped the screen, and the image paused. He looked up. "Has the news of Vincent's birth been released to the public?"

"Not yet," Varnay said. "I think—"

"Do it," Alexander said, getting to his feet. "I want the entire Federated Suns to be celebrating my son's birth, starting with Sekulmun. Captain Mallory?"

Cadmon came to attention. "Yes, my Prince?"

Alexander sat down and started pulling his boots on. "Call the palace's public-relations office. I want a press conference in twenty minutes. When you're done with that, I want you back here, in full dress uniform."

"Yes, my Prince."

"Is that a good idea, my Prince?" Varnay asked.

Alexander looked at his uncle in disbelief. "With everything that's going on? The people need some sign that there's hope in the future. Or is there some reason we should hide the birth?"

Varnay frowned slightly, then nodded slowly. "You're right of course, my Prince."

Alexander looked over at Cadmon. "Well, Captain?" he said. "I gave you an order. Get going!"

Still wearing his full dress uniform, Cadmon stood in the viewing hall and watched the streets fill up with happy and excited locals celebrating the news of the new heir. It was now late afternoon.

He had watched the First Prince deliver the announcement from just off camera. The dozen reporters, split between local ones and those following Alexander on his inspection tour, peppered the First Prince with questions that ran the political and economic gamut. The Prince had deflected the questions with a smile and mostly noncommittal answers, always steering the topic back to Vincent. By the time the press conference was over, word had spread across the city, and everyone's mood in the palace was jubilant.

A DropShip lifting off from the spaceport reminded Cadmon that word was spreading across the Federated Suns and beyond. It also started the clock running; Varnay had his heir, so there was no further need for Vincent's father.

Cadmon's earpiece buzzed. "Go for Six."

"Five here. The Prince is in his suite."

"Copy. Anything else?"

"Bambridge says he wants a bottle of Belisarius 2515 for the Prince's dinner tonight."

A layer of ice formed along Cadmon's spine. "White or red?"

"Red."

The chill he felt got stronger. "Send a page to the wine cellar," he said, keeping his voice level. "On second thought, send Deats along with the page. See if they have any Gold Sunburst beer."

Cadmon heard Sacco's tone change slightly. "Yes, sir. Full out?"

"As long as they can stand to attention in the morning."

"Right, sir. Thank you very much! Sacco out."

Cadmon forced himself to walk at a normal pace instead of running for his quarters. "Belisarius" was a code word for Theodora wanting a meeting, with the last three digits of the year indicating the time, fifty minutes from now. "Red" indicated the meeting was urgent.

Something was wrong.

Zahara's, despite it being only early evening, was already filled with people celebrating the new heir's birth when Cadmon entered.

Wearing the same clothes he'd used last time, he threaded through the crowd until he reached the bar. The same bartender was there, helped by two more. When he saw Cadmon, he jerked his chin toward the back hallway, Cadmon nodded, and headed down the back hallway.

As he reached for the handle to the storeroom, the door flew open and Theodora snarled, "Get in here!"

Cadmon stepped inside, and Theodora closed the door behind him. The room was dimly lit with a single glowstrip on a table near the door.

"What's wrong?" Cadmon asked.

"Plenty," Theodora replied, moving past him and into the center of the room. "You have to get the First Prince off-planet tonight!"

Cadmon tensed. "Why?"

"We've spotted Iron Wheel Triad members arriving at the spaceport in the last couple of days."

"I know them," Cadmon said. "The Maskirovka uses them for political disruption, assassinations, and sabotage missions."

Theodora's head moved enough for Cadmon to catch a flash of a well-formed chin and nose. "All of them are known to the March's security forces. They should have been picked up at the border!"

Cold certainty struck Cadmon. "Varnay!" he hissed.

"*He* brought the Cappies here?" Theodora hissed. "That's insane!"

"It's more likely he allowed them to pass through. Varnay replaced my people with his own a few hours ago. The First Prince's itinerary has had time to reach the Mask's ears, and Kalvin is crazy enough to try assassinating him."

"Varnay's letting the Cappies kill the Prince?"

"It's perfect. Laura Davion and her allies can scream until they want, but all the evidence, including the bodies, will point at Confederation involvement. Varnay has the heir and his niece as a rallying point. The people will want blood, which Varnay will use to cut into Laura's support base. If she wants to keep any influence, she'll have to support him. He launches a major offensive, focusing all the attention on the Confederation and maneuvering to be named Vincent's Regent."

Theodora shook her head. "Varnay's almost as despised in the Capellan March as the Cappies are."

"'Almost' being the key word. Anyone who opposes his call for Capellan blood gets painted as a Confederation supporter, and becomes either a prisoner or a nonentity."

Theodora was silent for several seconds, then nodded. "It makes sense."

"If Kalvin's people don't succeed, Varnay's will. Either way, you're right. The Prince needs to get off-planet tonight."

"Good. DropPad Twenty-Three North. DropShip's name is *Normandy Swallow*, Captain Dyubele. Liftoff is midnight."

"All right. Can your people run interference?"

"I'll talk to Justinian and see what we can do."

"Fine. I'm going to need a few hours to get things rolling. We'll move after sundown."

Theodora nodded. "Good luck."

"Thanks. We'll need it."

To most Federated Suns citizens, soldiers assigned to the First Prince's security detail had it easy. They stood guard a few hours a day, looked good in uniform, and followed parade-ground commands with precision.

What the civilians didn't know was that every member of Cadmon's team was a handpicked combat veteran, screened for loyalty, intelligence, adaptability, and mental stability. In addition to being trained bodyguards, each soldier had special skills; Cadmon and Sacco were both MechWarriors, while several others were armored-vehicle drivers and gunners. Two were combat medics, one was a sniper, another a hacker.

The security detail was already in action before Cadmon had even left for Zahara's. The code phrase "Gold Sunburst Beer" had started the preplanned operation, and each person knew their job. Supplies and weapons were gathered, escape routes scouted, and new communication protocols established. Bambridge, a retired Federated Peacekeeping Forces sergeant major, prepared the Prince.

Sacco was waiting for Cadmon at the door to his office. "Well?" Cadmon asked.

"We're green," Sacco replied. "Bad?"

"LSB bad."

Sacco scowled. The Limp Sword Boys, or LSB, was code for the Confederation. "Direct action?"

Cadmon nodded. "Have Sparks crack the spaceport's database and get IDs on every person who's landed in the last forty-eight hours. He's looking for Iron Wheel Triad members and Maskirovka agents. We're not moving until I know for sure."

"And if we don't find anyone?"

"Then call it a drill, but stay alert."

"It's bad, Captain."

Corporal Samuel "Sparks" Frees looked like a college student, not a soldier. While he had seen combat like the rest of the detail, his specialty was electronics, computers, and networked security systems.

"Define 'bad,'" Cadmon said. He was in a field uniform, with sidearm and helmet. The small room had him, Sacco, Frees, and a large amount of computer equipment crammed into it.

"There's thirty-plus Iron Wheel Triad members in the city, mostly Red Pole Enforcers. All arrived in the last two days." Frees tapped the computer screen, "These two are known Maskirovka assassins, and ranked high on DMI's kill list. They've been tied to five assassinations on this side of the border in the last decade."

"Theodora was right," Sacco said.

"Yeah," Cadmon said, biting the tip of his thumb. "Sparks, keep track of them. Call me if they get within half a klick of the palace. Also, monitor communications outside the palace for twenty square blocks."

"Yes, sir."

"We're going to need a fifteen-minute communications blackout inside the palace starting in ten minutes. The only comms I want clear are ours."

Frees grinned like a shark, the expression unnatural on his face. "Already on it, sir."

Cadmon returned his smile. "Good. Once we're out, get clear. Come on, Sergeant. Time to get the Prince back."

Cadmon, Sacco, and four Davion Guardsmen in full field gear marched into view of the First Prince's temporary security team. One of the four, the team leader, tried using his radio, but from the frown on his face, Cadmon knew the comms blackout was working.

The team leader stepped forward. "What are you doing, Captain?"

"The Prince's life is in danger," Cadmon said, his tone clipped and steady.

The guard snorted. "Bull."

Cadmon punched the team leader between the eyes, his comm gauntlets acting like brass knuckles. As the guard dropped unconscious, Sacco and the other soldiers pointed their rifles at the guards.

"Now," Cadmon said, his tone cool and steady. "As the Prince's security detail commander, I'm declaring a level Alpha-One emergency. That means we can use lethal force on anyone we deem a threat to the Prince. Right now, you three are a threat. You have five seconds to drop your weapons. Your choice. Five... Four..."

The three guards dropped their weapons.

Cadmon nodded. "Sergeant, riot cuffs. Get them inside the suite."

"Yes, sir."

Cadmon went to the suite's door and knocked, three long, three short, then three long again. As he finished, Bambridge opened the door. "Clear?" the valet asked.

"Aye."

The servant nodded, then looked back inside. "Time to go, my lord."

Alexander stepped out into the hall, followed by Bambridge. Both were dressed in Federated Peacekeeping Forces field uniforms. Alexander was wearing a helmet, and as he stepped out, Bambridge put on his own helmet.

"That bad?" Alexander asked as the bound guards were hustled inside the suite.

"Maskirovka assassins are on-planet," Cadmon replied briskly. "Varnay's security people are either stupid or they're ignoring them. Either way, we're leaving."

Alexander nodded. "Cynthia and the baby, will they be safe?"

"Safer than you are, my Prince," Cadmon said. "Varnay needs your son, and I requested extra security be sent to New Syrtis before we left."

Alexander nodded, but concern filled his eyes. "Good," he said. "Let's go."

They moved through the secondary and servant's hallways, picking up other Guardsmen holding important intersections and doors. Alexander and Bambridge, indistinguishable from any other Guardsmen, stayed just behind Cadmon.

"Guardian Two-Five to Guardian Six," Frees said in Cadmon's ear.

"Six here," Cadmon said softly.

"We have a situation," the corporal said. "In the last minute, three security cameras covering the west gate have gone down."

Cadmon raised his hand to stop the group. At once, the soldiers went on guard. "Natural or deliberate?"

"Deliberate. All on different circuits and locations. One maybe, two remotely possible, but all three? Negative."

"Any sign of the LSBs?"

"Not yet. I'm hacking into the surrounding buildings' security systems, but it'll take a few minutes."

"Any response from palace security?"

"Negative. I'm also checking the other gates." After thirty seconds, the corporal was back. "It's not good," he muttered. "Five more security cameras around the northern and southern gates are offline. Also, it looks like a crowd is gathering outside the palace."

Cadmon scowled. "Size and disposition?"

"Large and getting larger," Frees replied. "They're celebrating. Wait—I've identified three in the crowd as Iron Wheel Triad."

"The crowds are a distraction," Cadmon said. "The Mask is using them to get close to the palace."

A bell rang, echoing in the corridor.

"General alarm," Sacco said. "Primary exit is out."

Cadmon nodded. "Two-Five," he said into the radio, "pack it in. We're taking the secondary exit."

"No, sir," Frees said. "I'm going to stay."

"Sparks, I—"

"Sir, you need me to keep you appraised of the situation outside," the corporal said calmly. "And you're going to need me to cover you for as long as possible. Once you're clear, I'll slip out."

Cadmon sighed. "All right. Not a moment longer."

"No problem, sir. Rigging my escape route even as we speak."

"Good luck, Corporal."

"You too, sir."

Cadmon looked at his troops. "Alert the others. We're taking the secondary route. Gas masks ready."

"Gas masks?" Alexander asked.

"You'll see," Cadmon replied.

The secondary route passed through the city's sewers. The air was foul, requiring the gas masks. The walkways were slimy and slick, making each step a challenge. Fortunately, their helmets had night-vision capability, alleviating the need for flashlights.

After fifteen minutes of marching through sewage, Cadmon's comm bleeped. "Six here."

"Two-Five here," Frees said. "The crowd surrounding the palace is now twenty thousand strong, and half the palace's security cameras are dark. The crowds are occupying the guards and Varnay is— Wait." His voice came back after a few seconds, tense with worry. "Palace's internal security and communications systems are down. Someone's hacked the system."

Cadmon exhaled slowly, holding his hand out to stop the group. "The Mask is inside the palace."

"Yes, sir."

"Get going. Nothing more you can do there."

"There's one last thing I can do. I can change the security systems' access codes, then reboot it. It'll take their hacker time to respond."

"Do it, then get off-planet, back to New Avalon, and report to General Cantrick."

"Yes, sir. Good luck."

"You too. Six out."

"Does the plan change?" Alexander asked, having heard the whole exchange on the command channel.

"Not right now," Cadmon said. He looked at Sacco. "Sergeant, take two others and scout ahead. I want another three blocks between us and Varnay before we surface. That should also put us outside the Mask's containment zone."

"Yes, sir," Sacco replied. "Crocker, Towns, with me. Deats, McKillop, and D'Silva, rear guard. Obscure our trail, just in case."

Thirty minutes later, Cadmon climbed a cold, slimy ladder and emerged into a dark, narrow, trash-filled alley. It was raining steadily, reducing visibility. Sacco and the soldiers on point were guarding both ends of the alley.

"Sergeant?" Cadmon asked softly as he moved away from the opening.

"It's quiet, sir," Sacco replied. "Don't know for how much longer though. You want us to grab transport?"

"Three vehicles. Maximum protection for the Prince."

"Understood, sir. Crocker, Towns, with me." The three moved to the end of the alley, and after several seconds they darted across the empty street to the alley on the other side.

Another soldier came out of the manhole, and Cadmon reached down and roughly hauled him out, only to find himself staring at Alexander. "Sorry, my Prince," he said softly.

Alexander chuckled. "Don't worry about it," he replied. "Right now, I'm just a soldier under your command."

"All right," Cadmon said, pointing at the alley's unguarded end, "get over there and watch."

Alexander frowned. "Isn't that being a little paranoid?"

"That's what I'm paid to be," Cadmon replied with a tight smile. "Get going."

Ten minutes later, the last trooper climbed out into the alley and replaced the manhole cover. Another fifteen minutes passed before two cars and a van pulled up to the alley's mouth.

"Any problems?" Cadmon asked Sacco.

"None, sir," the sergeant replied.

The group scattered to the cars, and the convoy got underway. Cadmon, Alexander, Bambridge, and five troopers were in the van, the middle of the three-car convoy. One soldier drove, while D'Silva, the one riding shotgun, monitored police and military frequencies. The others sat and scanned both sides of the street and the rear.

Cadmon sat in the back with Alexander and Bambridge. "All right," he said to Alexander, "we'll stop close to the spaceport, then go the rest of the way on foot."

"Sir!" D'Silva said.

"What is it?" Cadmon asked.

"Police and military bands just blew up. I've got reports of firefights inside the palace, and Varnay's placed the militia on alert."

"Damn," Cadmon muttered. "As soon as he thinks about it, he's going to lock down the spaceport. Six to Five."

"Five here," Sacco said. "Pick up the pace, sir?"

"No choice."

"One-Three to Six."

"Go for Six. What is it, Deats?"

"Possible tail," said the corporal, who was riding in the third car. "Industrial truck, no markings."

Cadmon frowned. "How sure?"

"Seventy percent. They made the last two turns we did."

"All right. Guardian Six to all Guardians. Eyes open and don't hesitate to call out. Five, lead the way. Evasion plan Beta-Two."

"Copy, Six."

The van sped up, and every soldier except the driver checked their weapons.

"My Prince," Cadmon said, reholstering his pistol, "from this moment on, I don't want you more than an arm's reach away from me or Bambridge. Understood?"

Alexander nodded. He didn't look nervous, but his tone expressed worry. "Do you think it's the Mask?"

"Maybe."

The convoy made seemingly random turns at three intersections. They left the residential area and moved into an area of light manufacturing and warehouses. Traffic was light, the rain steady.

Inside the van, no one spoke, but the tension remained high. Cadmon's eyes never stopped moving, checking each trooper in the van, then the passing scenery, then back to his team.

After the fourth turn, Deats reported the truck was still behind them. Cadmon came to a decision. "Guardian One-Three, stop that truck. Guardian Five, head for the spaceport, best speed. Expect trouble." He tapped the van's driver on the shoulder. "Floor it."

The soldier nodded, and the van accelerated.

They shot through the next intersection, forcing several vehicles to slam on their brakes and lean hard on their horns. As they reached the other side of the intersection, Cadmon heard gunfire behind them.

"Guardian One-Three," he said. "Status?"

"Cappies!" Deats replied. "Truck's full of them!"

"Hold for as long as you can!" Cadmon directed.

The van shot into the next intersection at a high rate of speed, which saved it from being T-boned by a cargo truck. As it was, the truck slammed into the van's rear panel, spinning the lighter vehicle around, sending it onto the sidewalk and into a fence.

The impact tossed the van's occupants around. Cadmon landed on top of the Prince, their helmets clashing with enough force to stun both of them. Fighting dizziness and blurred vision, Cadmon tried pushing himself up, only to find his limbs tangled up with Alexander and Bambridge.

Gunfire from outside the car made him renew his efforts. A van window shattered behind him, showering him with glass fragments. He drew his pistol just as a hand grabbed his shoulder. He turned, bringing his pistol up, only to have Sacco shout, "It's me, sir! We have to move!"

With the sergeant's help, Cadmon got to his knees. "Stay down!" he hissed at Alexander. The gunfire was much louder now, and Cadmon

could see the cargo truck fifty meters away, flashes of gunfire coming from around the vehicles in the intersection. Half a dozen Guardsmen were trading fire with the enemy, one popping up from behind a car long enough to fire a grenade launcher at the truck. The truck's rear exploded, and Cadmon heard several screams.

With one side door blocked by the fence and the other too damaged to open, Cadmon had to pull himself through the window Sacco had broken. His vison was clearing, and while his head still hurt, his dizziness was gone. He stepped forward and raised his own submachine gun, firing a long burst in the enemy's direction. "Get the Prince out of here!"

He glanced back just as Sacco and D'Silva hauled Alexander out through the window. The Prince fumbled for his own gun, but both soldiers grabbed him by the arms and half carried, half dragged him toward the waiting car. Bambridge followed, his own gun up as he looked for targets.

The enemy's fire increased as they saw their target getting away. Cadmon and three of his troops stood their ground, forming a wall of flesh between Alexander and the enemy, firing back with discipline and accuracy. Two Guardsmen went down as bullets found them, but by then, Alexander was in the car. With a screech of tires, the car roared away and disappeared into the night rain.

"Pull back!" Cadmon grabbed the nearest downed soldier by his harness and dragged him behind the van. He changed magazines on his gun then peeked around the corner of the van. He could see only two other Guardsmen on their feet, one crouched behind the scant cover of a lamppost, the other using a signboard that wouldn't withstand any gunfire. The van was full of bullet holes, and he could smell gas.

At least the Prince got away, he thought.

"One-Three to Six!" Deats' voice was ragged. "We're coming in!"

Before Cadmon could ask what the corporal meant, two dark-blue APCs rolled into the intersection, turret-mounted machine guns pouring fire into the gunmen around the cargo truck. Hatches on the sides of the APC facing away from the enemy opened, and armed troops in dark uniforms leaped out and added their firepower to the APC's guns. In fifteen seconds, the enemy gunmen had either been killed, wounded, or scattered.

One figure was shouting orders and motioning to the others. The APC stopped firing, and a dozen troopers advanced toward the truck at a quick walk, weapons ready to fire. Once they were moving, the leader approached the van. Cadmon rose, his gun pointed at the ground.

The man stopped near the front of the van, rain dripping from his forage cap. "Good evening, Captain," a familiar voice said.

Cadmon scowled. "Ferryman."

"Where is the Prince?" the security consultant asked. "Is he in the van?"

"He's safe," Cadmon replied.

Ferryman relaxed. "Good." He took a couple steps forward. "You moved faster than I expected."

"Just doing my duty," Cadmon replied flatly. "McKillop, D'Silva, check on the others."

The two still-mobile soldiers ran over and checked the van and the bodies around it. Ferryman took another step forward, and Cadmon raised his submachine gun's muzzle so it pointed at the security expert.

"Your wounded need medical aid," Ferryman said. "There's a hospital three blocks away. Best on the planet."

"You're not getting the Prince," Cadmon said.

Ferryman smiled. "I don't want the Prince, and neither does Theodora."

Cadmon's eyes narrowed. "Who?"

"You know who. Now, unless you shoot me, I'm calling in medical aid for your soldiers." He spoke into his radio for a few seconds, then said to Cadmon. "You can't be around when the paramedics show up."

"Sir," D'Silva said. "Cooper's too injured to move. Hayman and Reece are dead."

"You're leaving me with little choice," Cadmon said to Ferryman.

A third APC rolled past the first two and stopped nearby. The side hatch opened, and Deats, his head wrapped in a bandage, leaned out. "Sir!"

Ferryman motioned his head toward the APC. "Get out of here, Captain. I'll take care of your people. The wounded will be treated, and your dead returned to New Avalon with honor."

"Why do you care?" Cadmon asked.

"Theodora sends her regards."

Cadmon lowered his submachine gun. "You're Justinian."

Ferryman smiled. "Get going, Captain."

Cadmon stepped inside the APC, followed by McKillop and D'Silva. One of Deats' troopers was behind the APC's wheel while the second manned the turret. Deats was standing in the infantry compartment. "You okay?"

"Fine," Cadmon said, sitting down on the bench.

He leaned back and closed his eyes.

DROPSHIP *NORMANDY SWALLOW*
SEKULMUN SYSTEM
CAPELLAN MARCH
FEDERATED SUNS
9 MAY 2525

Cadmon nodded to the two Guardsmen on either side of the hatchway, then rapped on the steel. After a few seconds, the hatch slid open, and Bambridge stood there. "Yes, Captain?"

"According to Captain Dyubele, we'll be docking with the JumpShip *Green Goddess* in twenty-seven hours."

"Cadmon?" a voice behind Bambridge asked. The valet stepped back, revealing Alexander sitting at the tiny fold-out table. Two card hands sat facedown on the table, along with a small pile of pennies. The First Prince was wearing a civilian shirt, trousers, and soft boots. He looked unhappy.

"Yes, my Prince?' Cadmon asked.

"Would you please join us? I need someone besides Bambridge to talk to."

"I—" Cadmon asked.

"I think you should, sir," Bambridge said.

Cadmon looked at the servant, who returned the stare with an impassive one of his own. He exhaled. "All right," he said, ducking inside the cramped cabin.

Bambridge stepped outside. "I need to check on something," he said. "I will be back shortly." The hatch slid shut, leaving Cadmon alone with the Prince.

"I never thanked you for saving my life back on Sekulmun," Alexander said. "You and your team."

"We did our duty, my Prince," Cadmon said.

Alexander glowered at him. "Will you knock off that 'Prince' stuff? When we're alone, call me Alex."

"But, my Pri—"

"*Alex,*" the Prince repeated. "After what you did, you've earned the right to call me by name."

Cadmon nodded. "All right...Alex. I noticed the three white roses in the vase when Varnay came to tell you the news of your son. How long had you known before he arrived?"

"Three hours," Alex replied. "Enough time to formulate the distraction plan with Bambridge. The roses arrived after Varnay replaced your people with his."

"I see." That explained why Cadmon hadn't been notified by his team. "An astute plan, my Pri—Alex."

Alexander smiled. "Was it that hard?" He motioned to the lower of the two berths. "Have a seat."

Cadmon sat, and Alexander turned to face him. "Now that we're clear of Uncle David's reach, what's our next move?"

"Getting you someplace safe," Cadmon replied. "Beyond that?" He shrugged. "That's not my decision."

"Which means it's mine?" Alexander leaned back in his chair and steepled his fingers in front of his lips. "There's a war coming," he said. "Uncle David and Aunt Laura were just looking for an excuse to start one, and now they have it—my disappearance."

"If you think that leaving you—"

Alexander made a short, chopping motion to cut Cadmon off. "I know you saved me, and I'm not going to argue that. Uncle David wants me dead, and he came this close to killing me. Aunt Laura may not want me dead, but she can't be trusted."

He leaned forward. "There will be war, and I can't do anything until I reach my majority and I'm free of the regents. Uncle David will cover up the assassination attempt because he can't afford a two-front war with his lack of trained troops. Aunt Laura has most of the Federated Peacekeeping Forces on her side, but she's no military strategist."

Cadmon nodded. "Do you have a plan?"

Alexander raised an eyebrow. "No," he replied after a few seconds. "As much as I want to, going back to New Avalon is out. Aunt Laura would use me as a figurehead, while Uncle David would use Vincent the same way. I will not put my wife and son in any more danger than I must. Right now, and I hate saying this, let's go to ground and wait it out."

Cadmon nodded. "My Pri—"

"Alex."

Cadmon nodded again. "Alex. We need to find a way to get word to members of the FPF High Command and—"

"No," Alexander said firmly. "Not until I hit the age of majority and can legally claim the throne of the Federated Suns on my own. No more regents, Cadmon. From here on out, for good or ill, I must stand on my own two feet if I am to claim the throne."

"You have my loyalty and the loyalty of my troops, sir," Cadmon said.

"I know, and I'm going to lean on you and them." Alexander smiled. "And because of that, I'm promoting you and every soldier in the detail one rank, effective immediately."

"But, my Pri—Alex, we only did our duty!"

"And did it damn well. I know it's a hollow reward right now, but we'll straighten it out after I reclaim the throne." He looked at Cadmon. "Right now, the only people I can trust are you, your team, and Bambridge. You deserve recognition for that."

"Once the Federated Suns citizens know you are alive and well, they will flock to your banner."

"Maybe. But until then, my only followers are Bambridge and my protection detail."

"We are yours to command, Alex."

"Good. That business is out of the way." Alexander grinned. "Now, do you know any new card games?"

UNIT DIGEST: KILLER BEES

JAMES BIXBY

Nickname: Stinging Schoolmasters
Affiliation: Mercenary (Twenty-First Centauri Lancers)
CO: Major Lynn Barrett
Average Experience: Regular/Reliable
Force Composition: 4 Reinforced Light Combined-Arms Companies
Unit Abilities: Camouflage, Gun it, Hit and Run, Unique Formation "Swarm Lance" (see *Combat Manual: Mercenaries*, pp. 50, 91)
Parade Scheme: With the Bees' reactivation, the unit's colors have returned to a dandelion-yellow body with black striping. Aerospace fighters use the traditional midnight blue of the Twenty-First Centauri Lancers' air wing, but paint their wings orange with red and yellow veins to evoke the image of tarantula hawks.

UNIT HISTORY

The Killer Bees are a modern incarnation of the rare thirty-first-century success story of fly-by-night mercenaries. Formed in 3025 by test pilots who sought more excitement, the Bees spent nearly thirty-five years developing a reputation of excellence as a Special Operations and Combat Search and Rescue command. During the Blakist Jihad, the Killer Bees staged rescues of the Second Star League's forces on Tukayyid. This triumph directly led to a merger with the depleted Twenty-First Centauri Lancers. After the Jihad, some veterans attempted to return to their roots as air-show performers sponsored by Cal-Boeing. Despite pride in the unit's origin with their company, Cal-Boeing retired the last Killer Bees Stunt Team in 3091.

The reactivation of the Killer Bees as a subunit of the Twenty-First Centauri Lancers was the brainchild of Lieutenant Colonel Thos Cardella, upon his return to the main body of the Lancers from the Republic of the Sphere. Being called on to put out fires throughout Prefectures VIII and IX, Cardella's battalion was often expected to do things a heavy BattleMech regiment was ill equipped for. More than once a hostage rescue, missing-persons search, or riot-response action would see most of the top-heavy Lancers sidelined while what few special forces and aircraft Cardella possessed coordinated with local police.

While creating a lighter-weight force more suitable for CSAR, rapid response, and cadre duty appealed to the Lancers' command, the reality of the unit's renewed contract with the Lyran Commonwealth and constant need to repair and refit from the predations of Clans Jade Falcon and Wolf sidelined the project. Only when the Lancers took a contract with the newly established Tamar Pact could they reestablish the Killer Bees.

On Pandora, the Bleeding Eagles and Burnt Offering mercenary commands neglected to coordinate with the Lancers, leading to several near fiascos. Finding the situation untenable, and needing to build and train the Tamar Pact Militia units, the Tamar Pact and the mercenaries' leadership reached a compromise. By combining the lightest assets of the Twenty-First Lancers into a subsidiary command and starting a healthy purchase and recruitment drive, the Killer Bees swarmed the Inner Sphere for the first time in nearly eight decades. The Bees were split into units on Arcturus, Pandora, Kelenfold, and Crimond, and were tasked with training local militias and familiarizing the Pact's smaller mercenary units with the Lancers' operational protocols.

Task Force Alpha went into training for the Arcturus Tamar Pact Militia with aplomb, seeing to the development of defensive doctrines against Clan Jade Falcon's mobile-warfare tactics as well as recent developments with Clan Hell's Horses' Horde and Ranger Clusters deployments. While equipment for the militias is trickling in, preparation is at least on par.

For the Killer Bees' secondary mission, Major Barrett's first target was the Bleeding Eagles, thanks to their role in getting her company needlessly bogged down on Pandora. As a mixed column of Eagles moved toward the staging area for the planned training exercises, Arrow IV missiles rained down across the Eagles' combined-arms group. Instead of bearing chalk munitions, the artillery rounds were canisters that spread dozens of liters of honey-flavored quillar syrup all over the 'Mechs, tanks, and rapidly dismounting infantry who believed themselves under attack. A meeting of the two commands after the action—and after much-needed showers—resulted in an airing of grievances, which led to agreements to better coordinate.

Not all mercenary commands have appreciated the effort to enforce the Lancers' command authority, however. After word of Major Barrett's honey-loaded artillery spread among units stationed on Arcturus, Burnt Offering prepared to stave off public humiliation. Prior to a training exercise involving the Arcturus TPM, Burnt Offering's armorers loaded live antiaircraft ammunition in the autocannons of their Partisan tanks. The *Queen Bee* was subject to return fire and had to make an emergency landing. The rest of the Killer Bees, believing Burnt Offering had broken their contract, immediately powered up their energy weapons and moved in to subdue the rogue command. After half an hour of hit-and-run combat, Burnt Offering surrendered and was arrested. Clan Sea Fox's Mercenary Bonding Commission is currently investigating the incident.

COMPOSITION

The Killer Bees' Table of Organization and Equipment largely mirrors how it was been laid out during the 3050s. The reality of being deployed on multiple planets to assist in training the Tamar Pact Militia has led to splitting the Bees into four task forces. Task Force Alpha, personally commanded by Major Barrett, is typical of such an arrangement. It consists of a light BattleMech lance, a platoon of VTOL-transported battle armor, a pair of aerospace fighters, and a reinforced attack-helicopter platoon. Of special note is the *Queen Bee*, a Planetlifter Tactical Support Aircraft that provides coordination for the entire task force. The *Queen Bee* is intended to be a command platform for the entire Killer Bees unit, but for the time being, it has remained on Arcturus with Task Force Alpha, and is escorted by Alpha's aerospace group.

ONE THOUSAND

ROB SCHUBERT

FORT BELODODIA
KANDERSTEG
ARC-ROYAL THEATER
LYRAN COMMONWEALTH
2 SEPTEMBER 3128

"That man either hates me, or thinks I have a bright future in the army. I'm not sure which," Hauptmann Greta Wellington declared dryly as she watched the Second Donegal's XO back up off the tarmac. Leutnant-Colonel Friedrich Steiner had simply driven up during the afternoon drills, explained that he had a special assignment for Greta, and acted like she should be honored. He'd excused himself, saying he had no time for questions.

Greta's First Battalion comrades, Hauptmanns Mehyar and Brewer-Shaw, made themselves very busy stowing their neurohelmets. She was sure they were taking advantage of the noise from exoskeletons and power tools setting up the parade grounds to laugh at her expense.

"Okay, okay," she conceded. "Go fraternize with all the archdukes and admirals you can handle. The anniversary is the only time anyone like that is ever coming to Kandersteg. But you better save me a plate with the good cheese."

"I give you my word as a member of House Brewer, your snacks shall stay untouched," Brewer-Shaw said with a theatrical bow.

"The duke's, like, your sixth cousin," Mehyar laughed, giving him a good-natured nudge. "Why do you think we call you Brewski instead?"

"He's got a point, but if you're willing to make promises like that..." Greta arched an eyebrow at him. "I'm not talking about the local stuff.

I want the imports from Furillo: Mont Vert or Ingrid's Own, something real fancy."

They made some noises of agreement as they left, but Greta suspected the snacks would last as long as a one-legged *Wasp*. Right now, though, it was time to get to work. The Second Donegal Guards were about to turn 1,000, and it meant...well, it meant a lot of work. There were other Guardsmen setting up stations all over the city for greeting the people and, of course, handing out recruitment material while everyone admired their shiny hardware. But for her, it meant an evening of parking 'Mechs in positions and poses meticulously dictated by a committee from the Department of Recruitment.

Ostensibly, the 'Mechs showcased color schemes of all the nations the Second had fought for—Terran Alliance, Protectorate of Donegal, Lyran Commonwealth, Star League, Federated Commonwealth, and Lyran Alliance—but the 'Mech selection was so deliberate in its attempt to equally represent every Commonwealth manufacturer that Greta felt like she was at a trade show. The pageantry surrounding Coventry Metal Works gifting a new *Gauntlet* to Greta's unit was proof of that.

"I'm glad nobody's grading us on historical accuracy," she said, looking up at a *Griffin* painted in the colors of the Royal Guard, ostensibly to represent the Lyran Alliance. "The only way you ever protected Archon Peter was from a warehouse."

It wasn't all wrong, though. Someone had at least remembered that the *Thunder Hawk* was originally a Star League Defense Force 'Mech, and made sure it was painted in SLDF colors. Since all these choices were made by people far above her, Greta supposed that, for the sake of her career, she would try very hard to decorate their party exactly how they wanted.

KANDERSTEG GENERAL ASSEMBLY
THUN
KANDERSTEG
ARC-ROYAL THEATER
LYRAN COMMONWEALTH
2 SEPTEMBER 3128

"Okay, Maddie, we'll open with a shot of you going through the main doors," Neil told her, making a minute adjustment to the way his holovid camera sat on his shoulder as its light flashed on.

Maddie did a last-minute check in her hand mirror, rearranging the dark locks she had meticulously chosen to escape her pinned-up hair in the hope it would make her look more spontaneous. She had enough time to free her temple locks and ensure her lapel pin was on straight before Neil spoke again. "And...we're rolling."

The news crew rounded the corner and entered the ornate faux-marble ballroom as Maddie put on her well-rehearsed "soft news" smile and faced the camera.

"This is K. Madeline Schroeder with the Donegal Broadcasting Company, reporting from the planetary capital here on Kandersteg," she said, keeping her voice light. "On the eve of their big millennial celebration, officers of the Second Donegal Guards are getting some time with Lyran dignitaries and their fellow soldiers in the Lyran Commonwealth Armed Forces. Many of the realm's most notable figures are here tonight, from Grand Duchess Claudia Steiner to Hauptmann-General Fredrick Hogarth. Local sources have also told DBC that Khan Patrik Fetladral is on-planet for tomorrow's ceremony."

Neil swept his holovid camera over the crowd on the ballroom floor, pausing momentarily to focus on anyone he might recognize as particularly important. There was a clear divide between high-level dignitaries, leisurely enjoying the party's lavish selection of food and drink, and LCAF personnel constantly rushing about to pass messages. Since the party itself was humming along, Maddie wondered if this meant something was wrong with tomorrow's events. If those didn't go down exactly the way the Archon wanted, it was going to destroy people.

"DBC will be featuring full coverage of tomorrow's events, so check your local listings. And trust me...you won't want to miss this one." She threw the camera one of the smiles she reserved for commercial bumpers and held it until Neil told her she was clear.

"I'll get this sent," he told her, tucking his camera back into its case. "The home office will have it on every screen from Terra to Timbuktu."

"Yeah, being associated with puff pieces *and* anniversary journalism, just what I always dreamed of..." Maddie sighed. "Hopefully this leads to a meatier assignment next time."

"We can only hope," Neil said. He headed for the door, and Maddie headed for the bar.

She maneuvered her way through a sea of elegant gowns, silk tuxedos, and dress uniforms, overhearing bits of conversation that would eventually bloom into the corporate acquisitions or government initiatives she hoped she'd get to cover someday. Local officials touted the value of Kandersteg to potential investors in melodious English while harried staff relayed instructions in the local Indonesian dialect. Two officers arguing over champagne took a step back from one another, and Maddie slipped between them to reach her destination.

A trio of junior LCAF officers in dress uniforms had set up shop near the end of the bar, the two men clearly deeper in the cups than their female companion. On closer inspection, all three wore the insignia of a hauptmann. The shorter man was tanned with short, dark hair, the other with a cleanly shaven scalp and skin the color of coffee with cream. The woman was the stereotypical Lyran lady, pale and wearing blond hair in a tight braid.

Maddie slid up beside them and motioned to the bartender. The three officers were having quite the laugh about something, and while she didn't mean to eavesdrop, she definitely overheard some of it.

"Hogarth would've been so mad about having to drive that *Griffin* he'd have keeled over on the spot!" the shortest of the trio said, and was met with roaring laughter from his companions. The man pantomimed a heart attack, spinning around. It only took a moment for him to look past his friends and notice Maddie watching his performance, and he froze the moment he spotted her DBC press badge. "...I hope that you could do me the favor of keeping that out of your story," he backpedaled, straightening his dress jacket. "My colleagues and I have nothing but the highest respect for our superiors, and Hauptmann-General Hogarth is no exception. We were merely..."

"Having a bit of fun." Maddie waved him off. "Don't worry, I'm not on the clock again until tomorrow. I'm K. Madeline Schroeder, from the DBC, by the way." Besides not wanting to cross the line from "journalist" to "snitch," Maddie knew mocking people above you was a sacred rite of people who worked for a living. Which, she figured, was as true of them as it was of her. None of them wore enough medals to make her believe otherwise.

"I knew you looked familiar," he said. "Hauptmann Naseem Mehyar, Second Donegal Guards. I work directly under Leutnant-Colonel Steiner in First Battalion's First Company—at least, until the Royal Guards approve my transfer."

"Greydon Brewer-Shaw," the bald man chimed in, "but everyone just calls me Brewski. "Second Company. Before you ask, yes, *those* Brewers, but not close enough to Vedet on the family tree for stock options in Defiance Industries."

"Greta Wellington," the woman said. "Third Company. I was in charge of setting up tomorrow's display 'Mechs, and my friends think it's some kind of...art form." She sipped a flute of champagne and made a show of rolling her eyes.

Mehyar offered their platter of hoarded snacks with a conspiratorial smile. After a moment of deliberation, Maddie picked a mini-quiche to pop in her mouth.

"Your secret's safe with me," she assured them. "But if you'd *really* like to secure my loyalty, you could tell me about some of your exploits. My bosses are always hungry for that kind of thing."

Brewski puffed himself up to let his jacket strain just a little at the buttons. "You want exploits? I bravely repelled the Khan of Clan Wolf-in-Exile in my righteous quest to secure snacks for my fellow officers!"

He jerked his head at a table at the far end of the room, where the upper crust sat. The CO and XO of the unit were seated on each side of General Hogarth, in a way that suggested he had pushed his chair between the two. Opposite him was the petite and matronly Claudia Steiner, Grand Duchess of Furillo, and next to her, the largest man Madeline had ever seen. He wore the gray leathers of the Exiled Wolves and red stars as his rank insignia, just in case his sheer physical presence was not enough to demonstrate his identity.

"I think you just showed me who I should *really* be talking to," Maddie said, indicating Khan Patrik Fetladral with her glass. "I would love to know what gets a Khan, even of the Exiles, to a formal party like this."

"Yeah, we've been wondering the same," Mehyar said, putting a fresh mug of lager to his lips. "Good luck asking him, though. The guy can't seem to get a moment free. He's had almost as many people in his ear tonight as our CO. And you didn't hear this from me, but it is impossible to keep Hogarth from talking over you."

Hogarth said something, and the people he outranked pretended to laugh.

"We can do you better than talking with Hogarth," Greta snorted. "Why don't you ride with me tomorrow? We're supposed to have some kind of reporters-in-the-cockpit thing for the exercises out on the range tomorrow. Honestly, you'd be doing me a favor. I'd rather pick who I ride with rather than trusting a supposedly random drawing."

"Emphasis on the 'supposedly,'" Mehyar laughed. "Everyone else is using it to trade favors. I heard the XO is riding with some other Gallery Steiner just to make his mom happy."

"You can never have enough favors to trade," Brewski nodded. "Vedet got me into the Nagelring, and all I had to do was promise to stop coming to Christmas."

The trio shared a laugh, and Maddie joined in. Their easy camaraderie was appealing...and made for a great story. While TBC and Nashan slobbered over the brass, she could cover the junior officers that made the LCAF work. She nodded to Greta. "I'd love to."

Greta extended her hand, and Maddie took it. "See you tomorrow."

FORT BELODODIA
KANDERSTEG
ARC-ROYAL THEATER
LYRAN COMMONWEALTH
3 SEPTEMBER 3128

Coventry Metal Works said the *Gauntlet*'s control console was not a step, bench, or footrest. Greta had chosen to disregard this advice, putting her feet up while she finished her leftover Verde walrus sausages and listened to Claudia Steiner's speech. Behind her was the rhythmic clicking of her passenger strapping into the jump seat.

Madeline had stuck her noteputer on the bulkhead to her left and held an analog notepad and pen in her hand. She seemed to be concentrating intensely. "Secure enough for a parade, I guess. Could you turn it up?"

Claudia Steiner's voice rose in the cockpit. Madeline watched on her noteputer as the Grand Duchess of Furillo stood relaxed at the podium, her young grandson Ludwig beside her. The banner of the Lyran Commonwealth was placed prominently throughout the grounds, but the Lyran Alliance, Federated Commonwealth, and even Terran Alliance flags made an appearance. More common than any but the Steiner fist itself was the Cameron Star, symbol of the long-disbanded Star League.

"...for that is what they are: Unwearied. When my grandfather found out they wanted to officially change this fine unit's nickname, he simply said no. There was no label more suited to them, he said, than the Unwearied Second. And that is why we are here today, to celebrate one thousand years of uninterrupted service, for which they have never needed rest." Claudia paused, and the crowd applauded, just as planned.

"If only he was still in charge," Greta cut in. "He didn't mark the nine hundredth anniversary with some fancy ceremony. He left his garrison post, jumped the Combine border, and ransacked a distillery. Spent a week in the stockade for it before the Archon pardoned him. Then he got out and threw one hell of a party. And he was SLDF, too."

"Star League fan, huh?" Madeline asked. "Not many of those left. *Especially* not for the second one. I was surprised they put up so many Cameron Star banners, given that your unit was SLDF for such a short time, but you must be quite pleased."

"Got that right. Born on Coventry, graduate of Coventry Military Academy. We still remember what that League meant." Greta heard Madeline jotting something on her notepad as she looked back to the stage, where Claudia Steiner had yielded the floor to the man of the hour, Leutnant-General Arnaud Zardetto.

"Seems nervous," Madeline said, zooming her screen in on him. "Look at his hands. He's gripping that podium like he's gonna tear it in half."

"Probably feels out of his element," Greta suggested. "The Old Man isn't one for speeches. Usually leaves the soapbox for the XO."

Three words into Zardetto's speech, Madeline spoke up: "Is that an orbital drop? If the LCAF wanted to dazzle the audience, they're probably succeeding."

Greta looked up to see red streaks burning their way down across the sky. Nobody had told her anything about this, so she switched on her comms. "Anyone heard anything about an orbital drop?" she asked, trying to keep the fear and excitement out of her voice.

"I'm seeing it too," Mehyar confirmed. "Traffic control hasn't heard anything. That means we have to assume targets are hostile."

Leutnant-Colonel Steiner's voice came through the radio to confirm her suspicion. "Hauptmann Mehyar is correct. Move to intercept unknown targets. Bogies cannot be allowed to breach the city perimeter."

"We won't let them get past us, sir," Greta said, immediately gripping the control sticks with eager hands. "Madeline, I know you only signed up for a ride to the range, but I don't have time to stop and let you out. You think you can keep cool?"

Madeline smiled back weakly. "Always wanted to do wartime correspondence. This will be my ticket to awards season, just watch."

Greta could see people on the parade grounds and the streets beyond being ushered out of the open by the same armored infantry who had just been basking in their adoration. As the frantic energy of a large group of panicked people bubbled up, Greta backed her *Gauntlet* off from the stage and turned around to the open land south of Fort Belododia. To the sides, her sensors called out Mehyar's *Griffin* and Brewski's *Thunder Hawk* coming alongside her, along with a *Caesar* piloted by Sergeant Nakamura, a pilot from Third Battalion. She quickly instructed the computer to tag them as her lancemates.

Her sensors pinged five incoming drop pods. Greta knew what kind of incoming targets came in groups of five, and she would be at a disadvantage against them in tech as well as numbers.

"When we make contact," Mehyar said through the radio, "Brewski, you and Nakamura let them come to you. Wellington and I will try to pin them in from the flanks. These Clanners want a fight, they'll get what they came for."

Greta signaled an affirmative, and when she pushed the throttle forward, her *Gauntlet* lunged like a dog off the leash. Off to the side, Mehyar's *Griffin* gave chase, with the other two trailing behind.

"Okay, Madeline," Greta said, raising her voice to stay above the rhythmic thump of the OmniMech's running, "when we get into the fighting, be sure to keep your feet up off the floor. I'm in a cooling suit and 'Mech boots, but you don't have either of those. If I have to push the heat levels up, there's a very real chance your shoes could melt to the deck. Besides that, just do what I tell you, and I'll get you back to the DBC in one piece, okay?"

"Can I record something while you drive?" Madeline asked.

The restraints on the pilot's chair kept Greta from shrugging. "If you want to shout over the sound of this thing running, I guess."

Behind her, Greta heard Madeline grab her noteputer and start recording. "This is K. Madeline Schroeder reporting from the Second Donegal Guards' millennial-anniversary celebration, where suspected Clan attackers have made multiple drops here on Kandersteg. Though the Lyran soldiers expected to be demonstrating their skills in the cockpit for a crowd of cheering onlookers, they're more than ready to meet whomever these uninvited guests are head-on."

OUTSKIRTS OF THUN

The *Gauntlet* slowed to a cautious walk once they spotted the first split-open drop pod. Several more littered the ground nearby, suggesting the raiders had dropped in an impressively tight formation. Greta swung the 'Mech wide to circle cautiously around the side, dipping into the woods for cover. Mehyar's *Griffin* rocketed over a stream in the distance and landed in the expanse of swamp beyond while they waited for their lancemates to catch up.

Five Jade Falcon 'Mechs were just touching down, all painted in a vivid green with yellow highlights.

"Command, this is Hauptmann Wellington," Greta radioed. "I have visual confirmation of one Clan Star. *Cougar*, *Grendel*, *Koshi*, *Thor II*, and *Loki*. Do you copy?"

"Hauptmann, this is XO Steiner," a crisp voice responded. "Confirming your sighting. They've dropped several more Stars around Thun. We're moving to respond, so your lance will have to hold until we can send reinforcements. Command out."

The Clan 'Mechs were already turning toward the fort and Thun as Brewski's voice came in over the radio. "Well, you heard Freddie." He laughed. "Who wants to call their shot first?"

Mehyar's blue-and-gold *Griffin* took that honor when he shot skyward, a trail of missiles raining down on the *Koshi*. "Pilot of the *Koshi*, this is Hauptmann Naseem Mehyar of the Second Donegal Guards. Since you decided to cross the border without naming yourself, shall I assume you are too cowardly to accept my challenge to duel?"

The boxy machine responded by twisting to fire its medium laser at him, all without missing a step, followed by the harsh sound of radio jamming. Greta switched back to the lance frequency, where Brewski was helpfully noting, "Well, guess playing things by the book is out. Let's put the squeeze on them, stop them from closing in on the city."

Greta ran parallel to the *Cougar*, letting a Thunderbolt missile rip as she did so. She faintly heard Madeline trying to narrate another recording from behind her, but Greta's world narrowed down to just her and the target. The little 'Mech shuddered under the massive missile's impact. She expected the pilot to turn about and return fire, so she kicked up her throttle to throw off the Clanner's aim. Instead, the *Cougar* stayed fixed on its path toward Thun, far more focused than the *Koshi*.

Brewski shifted his olive-drab *Thunder Hawk* into their path like a goalie. Before Nakamura's *Caesar* could even move alongside him, though, the full Star opened fire. The *Grendel* was fastest on the draw and sprayed a stream of autocannon slugs up the *Thunder Hawk*'s side. Farther back, the *Cougar*'s paired lasers etched gashes on the *Thunder Hawk*'s thighs. The *Thor* rained missiles from a distance, hoping to capitalize on any weakness with a PPC shot that ended up only chewing up dirt, but the *Koshi* found its mark, drilling both of its missile salvos into the assault 'Mech's center. Like an angry bear, Brewski focused on the oncoming *Loki* and erased the charging OmniMech with a trio of Gauss rifle slugs that blew a hole clean through its back, all while avoiding the incoming missile salvo and massive burst of autocannon fire.

"Team, I don't think they're after the city," Mehyar concluded, positioning himself between the *Grendel* attempting to circle down toward the swamp and Brewski's *Thunder Hawk*. "They're after Brewski."

"But why me?" Brewski asked, sounding more confused than afraid. "It's not like they'd get anything for me. Vedet doesn't like me enough for a ransom, doesn't hate me enough for a hit job."

Greta thumbed the trigger for her heavy particle projection cannon, and almost immediately she could feel the engine's heat rising through the floor. The *Cougar* shuddered again under Greta's shot as she lunged closer to it. The Clan pilot must've finally thought better of its focus on the *Thunder Hawk*, because the *Cougar* turned to face Greta and spat a staccato stream of beams and missiles into the onrushing *Gauntlet*. One missile exploded against Greta's canopy, not penetrating, but leaving a spiderweb in the middle of the ferroglass.

"It's not the pilot..." Greta said slowly as the pieces all clicked into place for her. "It's the paint! Remember reading about Operation Bulldog, when the Clanners would see Star League colors and fly into a rage?"

Mehyar's voice was low and focused, his *Griffin* now dancing in front of the *Grendel*, keeping himself between the Clanner and his intended target. "Good for the people in town, bad for Brewski."

The roar from the Clan 'Mech's autocannon echoed in his cockpit loud enough to come in over the radio.

"Well, all I have to do is fight the rest of them alone, right?" Brewski responded. "Should be easy, as long as I don't get shot more than..." The *Thor*, farther into the backfield, reminded him of its presence once more through long-range-missile and PPC fire. "...Okay, I think *that* was my limit." He started to backpedal, hammering the *Thor* with another pair of Gauss slugs, then firing the third at the *Koshi*.

If Star League colors were the problem, the *Thunder Hawk* was close to having resolved the issue, with its armor mostly chewed away by the constant barrage. What little protection it had left was largely on its legs, leaving its weapons mostly exposed and its fusion engine at risk.

Nakamura moved his *Caesar* directly into the line of fire and answered the *Thor*'s shots with his own, but the Clan pilot read the move and slipped to the side. The *Caesar* did manage to catch the barrage of fire from the *Koshi*, absorbing the cloud of short-range missiles it had spat out and rocking back under the blow.

"Hey, Brewski, wanna trade dance partners?" Greta asked. As the *Cougar* tried to back away and refocus on Brewski, Greta jammed her throttle forward as hard as she could, triggering the 'Mech's Myomer Accelerator Signal Circuitry system and bringing the supercharger roaring to life. Rather than staying tight on the smaller 'Mech, she rushed ahead to close the distance with the towering *Thor*.

The hammering blows of the larger 'Mech's missiles and autocannon rounds sounded like massive hailstones on a roof as she jammed both triggers. Her PPC and Thunderbolt launcher hit back even as the *Thor*'s own PPC skimmed over her right side with a blinding blue flash. In the distance, the *Grendel*'s pilot ejected out of the cockpit as the boxy 'Mech slumped down like a broken doll. Mehyar's *Griffin* stood over it, now missing its entire right side.

"Got one" he reported, "but I'm pretty sure the Royal Guards are gonna blacklist me for wrecking their loaner."

"Bah, I'm getting us all into the SLDF after this, for how gallantly you're defending the honor of this hallowed institution," Brewski said, managing to affect a joking tone even as his 'Mech seemed to be coming apart around him.

"Don't treat them as jokes," Greta snapped as she attempted to dance past the *Thor*'s line of fire. "They *were* heroes. Anyone from Coventry can tell you that."

The Clan 'Mech nimbly twisted to follow her, then rocketed skyward on its jump jets, firing its PPC again.

Greta saw a warning light flash for her 'Mech's left arm and heard the creaking of stressed metal. She pivoted on the *Gauntlet*'s foot toward the *Koshi* and let the Clanner have it with both barrels. The PPC chewed through the rear armor and the follow-up Thunderbolt missile lanced clean through its back and out the front. But before she could tell Brewski he owed her, the *Thor* fired a burst of cluster rounds straight at her. She had just enough time to notice her canopy had cracked open, and her chest felt very wet.

Greta was fighting. Fighting the *Thor*, to keep the *Gauntlet* on its feet, to keep her hands on the controls, to breathe. The Falcon 'Mech stood and simply watched for a moment. Greta could hear the Clanner's mocking laughter, and it sounded like when Brewer talked about the Second Star League. She tried to respond, to yell back at the enemy, but her breath didn't feel sufficient. As she tried to raise her *Gauntlet*'s arms to fire back, the *Thor* fired a single laser into her right arm, and the PPC mounted there fell with a groan of metal. Then the Thor simply walked straight up to the *Gauntlet* and gave her a push.

Greta heard someone shout in surprise. She had forgotten she had a passenger, maybe because when she turned her head, the corners of her vision were too dark to make anything out. All she could do was try to gasp out a warning.

"Buck...le up..." she choked out. When she coughed, she felt something wet come with it.

As the *Gauntlet* tipped over backward, Greta no longer had the strength to grip her controls. Her gyroscope should have been keeping the 'Mech upright, but it wasn't, and she couldn't figure out why.

The 'Mech hit the ground with a thunderous impact, and Hauptmann Greta Wellington let out a last, rattling breath.

Intellectually, Maddie knew she'd lost consciousness, but it felt like the world had been switched off and back on. The cockpit was now dark, and the back wall had somehow become the floor, but the sounds of gunfire were just as loud.

She wondered if she had been unconscious for hours, but when she brought her head up to look out the splintering canopy, she saw not a night sky, but the barrel-chested form of Brewski's armless *Thunder Hawk* silhouetted against pre-dusk clouds. A pair of alarmed voices were calling through the radio, but she couldn't make them out over the ringing in her ears, let alone reach the console, which was now several meters above her. Greta's limbs were dangling slack, still swaying slightly from the fall. When Maddie finally mustered the courage to reach out and touch her, she knew Greta was gone.

With Brewski's 'Mech in such battered shape, Maddie could actually see the capacitors flash when he fired his Gauss rifles. Whatever he was shooting returned fire, triggering a sudden electrical *pop*. The *Thunder Hawk* crumpled over to the side, a rocket trail launching through its cockpit toward the swamp to the west.

The *Gauntlet*'s long, gray-blue snout blocked much of the view above her, but she could see the crippled form of half a *Griffin* staggering toward her while shots flew overhead. Mehyar's battered 'Mech tried to deter the oncoming *Cougar* with what little weaponry it had left, but the last fight had been too costly.

Maddie unhooked her restraints and hopped up to grab the edge of the canopy. Splintered ferroglass bit into her fingers, but she gritted her teeth and pulled up, hoping to spot an emergency-exit latch.

Instead, she saw the *Thor* that had killed Greta and downed Brewski standing over the prone form of Nakamura's round-bodied *Caesar*, now down to a single leg. The *Caesar* raised the PPC in its arm and fired, the shot burying itself dead center on the *Thor*. A yelp slipped from Maddie's lips as she lost her grip on the canopy edge, leaving her once again limited to the view directly above her. She thought the rate of fire was intensifying, but instead of facing what was out there, she tried to focus on cleaning up the cuts on her fingers.

Some kind of winged 'Mech flew straight over the growing pile of ruined war machines. Maddie heard the telltale sound of missiles raining down as five large, armored figures detached from it in mid-flight, riding exhaust streams to the ground. She may not have been able to identify the 'Mech, but she knew an Elemental Point when she saw one, and she knew what one meant for downed pilots.

She looked around the cockpit for a weapon, or at least a metal bar she could yank off and use as a club. After a moment of panic, she realized one was right in front of her.

Greta's legs were now dangling free off the side of her pilot's chair, just out of arm's reach. Tucked in the heavy boot was the LCAF's standard-issue sidearm. Maddie mentally apologized to the dead MechWarrior as she jumped for it, swatting at the weapon to knock it loose. She had no luck on her first attempt, or her second. On the third, she saw a dark figure nearing the canopy glass, and fear gripped her heart.

"Okay, I am *really* sorry for this one," Maddie whispered, jumping and grabbing the whole boot. To her relief, the buckles gave way before Greta's ankle did, and the whole thing fell free. She scrambled to grab the pistol and tried to hide beneath the pilot's seat.

The intruder peeled open the cockpit above her, announcing their entrance with the screech of metal.

The Elemental activated a spotlight, and Maddie could tell the trooper was looking at Greta's body. She spun out from behind her hiding place and, just like she'd seen in all the action holovids, pulled the hammer back on her pistol.

"Hold it right there!" she ordered.

The Elemental raised their claw in a gesture of surrender as the battlesuit's body tipped to the side slightly to imitate a curious tilt of its head, a pantomime of friendliness.

"If I had wished you dead, that weapon would make no difference, *quiaff*?" The Elemental's booming voice asked. "No matter, I am not your enemy." He—Maddie now realized it was a "he"—pointed to the Wolf symbol on his armored suit's shoulder.

When Khan Patrik Fetladral revealed his face, inadvertently highlighting just how little size the battle armor added to his massive body, Maddie knew how utterly impossible it would have been to fight him with any length of pipe. Even the idea of shooting him with the pistol was foolish; she was sure this monolith could crush her windpipe long before she could shoot him enough times to kill. But when he extended the laser on his suit's right arm, it wasn't to kill her, but for her to grab onto.

The exertion of lifting her out barely registered on the Wolf Khan's face as he swiftly yanked her up and out of the cockpit. "Someone will come to collect you shortly," Fetladral said. "Stay here."

His faceplate snapped back down, and he bounded from one fallen 'Mech to another until he reached the *Thor,* now on its back and smoking from holes in its torso. Two more Elementals were tearing open the *Thor*'s cockpit, and Mehyar's *Griffin* stood watch as the final two cut into the fallen *Cougar.* Farther away, a trio of massive Gürteltier tanks rolled past an *Atlas* repeatedly kicking the ruined *Loki.*

Maddie noted the shooting had stopped as the winged 'Mech she'd seen earlier stood triumphantly amid the wrecks on the field. Then she realized why it seemed familiar—the Second's commander drove a captured *Flamberge*; she'd read that when she was researching the unit. She started to scoot down the side of the *Gauntlet*'s flat face before lowering herself down by her arms to drop to its hip. From there, she jumped to a nearby tree, shimmied down it, and ran toward the *Flamberge.*

It twisted to face her, and for a moment, she felt the same fear she had when the *Thor* had looked at her through the canopy, but she didn't let it slow her down. After a moment's hesitation, the towering 'Mech knelt, and its cockpit popped open, allowing Leutnant-General Zardetto to deploy a ladder and descend to her. Though he still towered over her after he touched the ground, she charged up to him and leveled an accusing finger. His lips pursed under his neatly trimmed gray mustache, and the crease between his brows deepened as he looked at her.

She had so many questions in her mind, all ready to *really* blow this story open. Did they have advance intel on this attack? Did they choose to incorporate the Star League imagery to deliberately incite Clan action? Was driving the *Thunder Hawk* some kind of punishment? And why did they do so little to aid their officers in combat?

Instead, what came out was less eloquent. "Just...what the hell was all this?"

"Even in a time of peace, the Jade Falcons hate our history and our way of life," he said, as if that explained everything. "But we stopped them."

"You *knew*?" Maddie shouted back. "You didn't warn them, but you knew?"

General Zardetto shook his head. It was a very controlled motion, once slightly to the left and then to the right. His expression held firm. "I had *suspicions* they would arrive," he corrected her. "But it was decided to keep the situation quiet rather than stir up panic on such an important day."

"So, what, you threw a party and just waited for them to show up so you could play hero?"

Zardetto frowned. "*You* told them about it. Result of an open society, people talk. But let's not forget, there were people in place, and they held. You work in a visual medium, so you can understand. Nobody wants to see a party where everyone has to hide behind an army while they do it. Reminds everyone of the Jihad. It is...important that we go forward without fear."

Maddie saw Brewski approaching in the distance, riding shotgun in a medic truck with a bandage over his eye. "And this is ensuring we live without fear?" she asked. "Using Star League colors to hang a 'shoot me' sign on unknowing pilots? How many people went into battle knowing they'd been volunteered to draw fire?"

The general looked past her to the wrecks of the *Gauntlet* and *Thunder Hawk*. He breathed out and seemed to shrink just a hair. "Holovids aren't the only ones who have to deal with sponsors. My job today was to execute policies set by the Triad. I was hoping it wouldn't come to this, and I regret what it cost my soldiers. Never doubt that. But I had a job to do."

"I'm going to do my job, too," Maddie said. Her head swam with anger. "I'm going to give everyone the facts of what I saw. Not the story that your recruiters want." She turned away to flag down the truck.

"Which agency were you from, again?" he asked, his tone once again practiced, like the first answers she'd gotten.

"The DBC. Go ahead and call my editor, I don't care."

"That's not my intention. It's just that the Archon will be *very* interested in the content of your story," he said with practiced casualness. He'd been off script before, but now he was back to reciting someone else's words, maybe even those of Archon herself. "She'd like to append a statement to your broadcast, and I've been asked to do the same. And the LCAF would like to assure you that we are looking forward to working with you again, depending on the public reception to your piece. I can provide you with my contact information, if you'd like."

He held out a card.

Maddie looked down at it and struggled to think about journalistic ethics rather than history lessons about Archons with names like Claudius and Katherine.

Then, with one bleeding hand, she grasped the card between trembling fingers and tucked it in a pocket.

CHAOS CAMPAIGN SCENARIO: AM I MY BROTHER'S KEEPER?

MATT LARSON

The end of the twenty-sixth century, still glowing in the smoldering ashes of the Reunification War, saw inter-imperial cooperation at an all-time high. The Capellan Confederation and Free Worlds League signed the Treaty of Geneva in 2556, which allegedly resolved the Andurien Crisis and set the stage for the founding of the First Star League. Thus, Ian Cameron believed, one of the most violent regions from the Age of War had been stabilized. The Freebooter's War in 2584–2588 posed an imminent threat to that peace, but Houses Liao and Marik avoided previous escalations, and at least were able to agree with whom the monopoly on violence rested.

Despite this, neither nation considered the covert battle for control over border worlds so resolved. The establishment of Kallon's RFL-2N *Rifleman* line in the treaty year made Asuncion a glittering prize within the grasp of the Mariks' ever-expanding ambitions. No sooner had the first modern *Rifleman* marched off the assembly line than operatives from the National Intelligence Agency (the forerunner of SAFE) flooded over seemingly every centimeter of São Paulo, Asuncion's capital. Overzealous propaganda spread by these operatives, including fabricated orders that pro-Marik citizens would be shipped off-world, exploded into planetwide violence in the spring of 2599, with bands of rioters targeting Capellan nationals. Militia reprisals added to the quickly spiraling violence. The Cameron dream of a unified humanity teetered dangerously close to the brink.

—FROM *DARK LABYRINTHS BENEATH: SHADOW WARS AND THE BIRTH OF MODERN STATECRAFT FROM THE THIRD ANDURIEN WAR TO THE AMARIS COUP*, NEW AVALON FREE PRESS, 3059.

TOUCHPOINT: SERVING TWO MASTERS

This scenario can be played as a stand-alone game or incorporated into a longer campaign using the *Chaos Campaign* rules (available as a free download from https://store.catalystgamelabs.com/products/battletech-chaos-campaign-succession-wars).

For flexibility of play, this track contains rules for *Total Warfare* (*TW*), with *Alpha Strike: Commander's Edition* (*AS* or *AS:CE*) rules noted in parenthesis, allowing the battle to be played with either rule set.

Major William Sutherland's comm crackled to life. "Transmission code October Romeo Five-Five-Zero. This is Sierra Lance, over."

Sutherland could hear an unusual amount of tension in Sergeant Hendry's voice. Something was off. "Go ahead, Sergeant."

"This—this was not in the intel report, sir." Hendry was openly frustrated, something else this trusted lance leader rarely exhibited.

"Explain," Sutherland said.

"Sir. The defenders. It's the Second Kearny."

"Say again, Hendry." Sutherland's mind raced back to all the briefings. The Second Kearny Highlanders wasn't supposed to be anywhere close to Asuncion. This operation was meant to be a show of force by the inevitable will of the Star League Defense Force to an audience of militia and rioting rabble, not against natives of Northwind.

"Definitely the Second Kearny, Major," Hendry said. "A lot of them."

"Understood, Sergeant. Your sister is in the Second, yes?" Virtually every soldier from Northwind under Sutherland's command knew someone in the Second Kearny Highlanders; family, friends.

"Aye, sir. I pray she's not here. But there's something else. Leviathan is on location."

Sutherland swallowed hard. Leviathan was the moniker he had given his brother-in-law's Highlander.

"Report received, Sergeant. Keep eyes on the situation. We are moving up immediately."

Sutherland cursed. *The sons and daughters of Northwind had stayed out of each other's way for 300 years, and it was on his own watch that such a damned thing had come to pass.*

SITUATION

VALE DAS SOMBRAS
ASUNCION
CAPELLAN CONFEDERATION
12 MAY 2599

The nascent Star League, unwilling to allow defiance of the founding accords to go unpunished, angrily demanded that the Capellan Confederation and Free Worlds League both stand down. When both the Capellans' and Free Worlds' intelligence services ignored the order, the Star League Defense Force quickly deployed multiple I Corps elements that had been freshly rebuilt after the Reunification War, notably the Thirty-Third Striker Regiment, which had been staffed by volunteers from Northwind. All participants of this uprising would have to be taught a lesson.

Major William Sutherland's battalion pressed into the Vale das Sombras, a sparsely vegetated valley north of São Paulo, to target a militia ammo dump in order to curtail militia activity. Unbeknownst to the SLDF, the Capellans had moved the Second Kearny Highlanders to Asuncion in April to put down the uprising. An accidental confrontation no one asked for seemed inevitable.

GAME SETUP

Recommended Terrain: Desert Oasis (*Map Pack: Deserts*), Forward Base (*Map Pack: Grasslands*)

The Defender arranges two mapsheets with the long edges touching. The Defender's home edge is the long edge of the Forward Base mapsheet. The Attacker's home edge is opposite, on the Desert Oasis map. The ammo dump is contained within hexes 1209, 1210, 1309, 1310, and 1311. A comms center is in located in hex 1013.

If using a map without buildings printed on it, or using *Alpha Strike* terrain, the Defender chooses east or west as their home edge, with the Attacker's home edge as the opposite. Designate a multi-hex, Level 1 Heavy Building (CF 90) covering five hexes, at least three hexes from their home edge (*AS*: 10" in diameter and 6" from the Defender's home edge, CF 8). Additionally, place a single Level 1 Medium Building (CF 40) at least five hexes from the Defender's home edge (*AS*: 2" in diameter and at least 10" from the Defender's home edge, CF 3).

Attacker

Recommended Forces: Thirty-Third Striker Regiment, SLDF I Corps, have Veteran skills and deploy up to a company of medium and heavy 'Mechs and up to six platoons of motorized or mechanized infantry. The Attacker also deploys one Mobile HQ with Gunnery 5, Piloting 6 (*AS*: Skill Rating 5) and Major William Sutherland in an HGN-732 *Highlander* with Gunnery 2, Piloting 3 (*AS*: Skill Rating 2).

The Attacker enters the battlefield from their home edge during the Movement Phase of Turn 1.

Random Allocation Tables: SLDF Highlanders, SLDF (*Era Digest: Age of War*, pg. 22)

Defender

Recommended Forces: Muir's Battalion of the Second Kearny Highlanders, mercenaries in the employ of the Capellan Confederation, have Regular skills and deploy at 150% of the Attacker's strength, utilizing a mix of 'Mechs, combat vehicles, and infantry. The Defender was not expecting a heavy force at this location, and is mainly comprised of light and medium units. The Defending units are led personally by Major Sean Muir, who was on-site preparing the base defenses. Muir pilots his own HGN-732 *Highlander* with Gunner 3, Piloting 4 (AS: Skill Rating 3).

The Defender may position their units anywhere within ten hexes (*AS*: 20") of their home edge before the start of Turn 1.

Random Allocation Tables: Mercenary Highlanders, Capellan Confederation (*Era Digest: Age of War*, p. 22)

WARCHEST
Track Cost: 350

OPTIONAL BONUSES

+50 Full Moon / Glare (Attacker Only): See pg. 56, *Tactical Operations: Advanced Rules* (*AS*: +2 to all weapon attacks).

+50 Expert Marksman (Defender Only): See pg. 155, *Campaign Operations* (*AS*: Half of the Attackers gain the Marksman SPA; see pg. 97, *AS:CE*).

OBJECTIVES

They'll See it from Space! (Attacker Only): Destroy designated ammo dump buildings. **[30 per building destroyed]**

Eavesdropping (Attacker Only): The Attacker's Mobile HQ must finish an End Phase within six hexes of the radio tower. **[200]**

No Trespassing! (Defender Only): Prevent the destruction of the designated ammo dump buildings. **[30 per building not destroyed]**

Impound Lot (Defender Only): Immobilize the Attacker's Mobile HQ. **[100]**

Family Matters: Avoid destroying or crippling enemy units. **[-25 per unit destroyed or crippled]**

SPECIAL RULES

Awkward Future Gatherings

Either side that destroys more than 25% of the enemy's force immediately loses the scenario. Units destroyed by ammo-dump explosions (see *Improper Packing* below) do not count toward this total.

Forced Withdrawal

All units adhere to Forced Withdrawal rules (see p. 258, *TW*; p. 126–127, *AS:CE*).

Improper Packing

When an ammo dump building is destroyed, the Attacker rolls 2D6. On a 9+, the building explodes and causes 100 points of Area-Effect damage to any units within the hex and 50 points of Area-Effect damage to units or buildings in adjacent hexes (*AS*: 3 points of damage to any units or buildings within 2", and 2 points of damage to any units or buildings within 4").

There Can Be More Than One!

If either side's *Highlander* is destroyed or crippled by enemy fire, the side that destroyed or crippled the *Highlander* automatically loses the scenario.

AFTERMATH

Refusal to directly engage his homeworld brethren quickly locked Major Sutherland's force into a long-range engagement. Encrypted messages, later unsealed, revealed a tense exchange between a frustrated Sutherland and a sympathetic but unyielding Major Muir that uncovered a tacit but mutual agreement to avoid a direct confrontation. After the failed operation, Sutherland was reassigned to command an infantry training battalion on New Earth and was forced into retirement by 2610. He then returned to Northwind and reentered service as a mercenary officer with the Highlanders.

The incident itself led to the SLDF immediately shifting regiments laden with Northwind volunteers away from the Capellan Confederation, and a wave of required loyalty oaths administered to officers prevented another such incident. Meanwhile, the Capellans were allowed to put down the lightly armed bands of resistance fighters quickly and violently. They destroyed any organized support for the Free Worlds League by executing the leaders of the uprising and banning pro-Marik parties. Asuncion would not fall to House Marik until well into the twenty-ninth century.

RANDOM ALLOCATION TABLES

BATTLEMECHS

2D6 Roll	SLDF Highlanders	Mercenary Highlanders
2	GLT-3N Guillotine [70] (RSFP:Wave2)	OSR-2C Ostroc [60] (3039)
3	LNC25-01 Lancelot [60] (RSFP:Wave2)	SCP-1N Scorpion [55] (3039)
4	TDR-5S Thunderbolt [65] (AGoAC)	FRB-2E Firebee [35] (3075-AW)
5	LCT-1V Locust [20] (AGoAC)	HBK-4G Hunchback [50] (RSFP:Wave2)
6	GRF-1N Griffin [55] (BB)	WSP-1A Wasp [20] (RSFP:Wave1)
7	WVR-6R Wolverine [55] (AGoAC)	SHD-2H Shadow Hawk [55] (AGoAC)
8	PXH-1 Phoenix Hawk [45] (RSFP:Wave1)	STG-3G Stinger [20] (RSFP:Wave1)
9	WSP-1A Wasp [20] (RSFP:Wave1)	GRF-1N Griffin [55] (BB)
10	ON1-K Orion [75] (RSFP:Wave2)	RFL-2N Rifleman [50] (XTRO Primitives IV)
11	ARC-2R Archer [70] (RSFP:Wave1)	CPLT-C1 Catapult [65] (AGoAC)
12	THG-11E Thug [80] (RSFP:Wave2)	TDR-5S Thunderbolt [65] (AGoAC)

VEHICLES

D6 Roll	SLDF Highlanders	Mercenary Highlanders
1	Manticore [60] (3039)	LRM Carrier [60] (3039)
2	Merkava Mk VIII [75] (3075-AW)	SRM Carrier [60] (3039)
3	LRM Carrier [60] (3039)	Condor [50] (3039)
4	Turhan [50] (3075-AW)	LTV-4 [50] (RG27)
5	Condor [50] (3039)	Marsden II-A [60] (3075-AW)
6	Alacorn Mk IV [95] (3058-C)	Goblin [45] (3039)

RECORD SHEET SOURCES

3039: Record Sheets: 3039
3058-C: Record Sheets: 3058 Unabridged, Clan
3075-AW: Record Sheets: 3075: Age of War
AGoAC: A Game of Armored Combat
BB: Beginner Box
RG27: Recognition Guide: IIClan, Vol. 27
RSFP:Wave1: Record Sheets: Force Packs, Wave 1
RSFP:Wave2: Record Sheets: Force Packs, Wave 2
XTRO Primitives IV: Experimental Technical Readout: Primitives, Vol. 4

NEVER TRUST THE RECRUITMENT POSTERS

JAMES KIRTLEY

GALATEA CITY
GALATEA
LYRAN COMMONWEALTH
1 JUNE 3025

You know, it's funny, but I always thought Galatea would be nicer than this. Maybe it was all those ads with gorgeous people in skimpy outfits leaning on BattleMechs while downing cold beers. Maybe it was the way all the other kids back home talked about it as if it was some weird Mecca (whatever *that* is). Maybe it was the way Dad always forbade me from taking the family 'Mech there to try making a living. You know what they say about forbidden fruit—although seriously, who forbids their kids from eating fruit? Anyway, I always imagined Galatea as having perfect weather and clean streets and stuff like that.

That is *not* what Galatea is like. Galatea is *hot*. Like, really hot. Like "Don't touch the metal parts of your 'Mech or you'll flash-fry to them" hot. And while it's a former Terran Hegemony world, it's not like the place is all high-tech and stuff. Heck, in half the places I've visited, the A/C doesn't even work. And those gorgeous people in skimpy outfits? Yeah, they're all wearing combat boots and frumpy jumpsuits with sweat stains everywhere. Nobody is attractive in that. So right now I'm envisioning the models from those ads in a holovid studio on Tharkad, gloriously freezing their skinny little butts off.

So. Why am I on Galatea, then? I mean, if the weather is so crappy and all?

Well, if you're a hopeful up-and-coming mercenary with a 'Mech and a few C-bills, it's pretty much the only place where you can go to make a living. Well, there's also Solaris VII, but that racket is *nuts*. Like, "Hey, Mom and Dad! Yeah, sorry I've been in system for a week and haven't sent you a message yet, but these calls are expensive. Oh, yeah, I had my first 'Mech bout! And, um, about Grandpa's *Locust*..."

So I'm on Galatea, which is famous for its mercenary hiring hall. Except that I've spent maybe ten minutes there in the week I've been on planet. The hall itself is pretty nice. It's all marble with columns and stuff, and the A/C works and everything. I go in there and stand in line, and someone makes me fill out a form with my information, like "Do you have a 'Mech?", and "What model is it?", and "When was the last time anyone fired up the fusion engine, and do they have cancer yet?"—that sort of thing.

Once I've filled out that form, they add me and my ride to a long list of mercs looking for work. My guess is that's the way mercenaries have been hired since time immemorial—except that maybe in ancient times people wrote down their comm codes and what kind of sword they had in fat marker on little slips of paper or something.

Heck, at least I *have* a 'Mech. Most folks here don't even have that. Those are the poor sods who get handed a rifle and are told to go after the guys who *do* have 'Mechs. I can't imagine how crap your life has to be before you sign up for that. I mean, don't get me wrong, I can totally see why people sign up to be groundpounders in militias and stuff, fighting for home and country and all. That I get. Doing it for a lousy C-bill? Let me tell you, there is not enough *nope* in the galaxy for that, if you know what I mean.

I know what you're thinking. "You have a 'Mech? That's awesome! What kind?"

Well, since you're asking... Remember earlier how I was joking about Grandpa's *Locust*? Yeah. Not so funny, really. But hey—at least I've got a *Locust*. It's a classic, one of them -1V models with the big underslung laser and the machine guns in the stubby little T-Rex arms. Sure, it doesn't pack a lot of punch, but it's quick, got decent armor for its size, and there's generally better targets out there, so it's relatively survivable.

I wasn't kidding about it being Grandpa's 'Mech, either. He grew up on Kalidasa and signed up to join the Free Worlds League Military. Apparently he tested real well or something, and they assigned him to a recon company in the Fifteenth Marik Militia, even gave him a shiny new 'Mech, fresh off the assembly line on Gibson. Most of the time he just ran around looking for bad guys, and when he found them, he'd call in reinforcements. Maybe he'd try to take a run-by shot at rear armor or something, but for the most part, fighting wasn't his primary job description.

Until, of course, you run into infantry. Those little popguns in a *Locust*'s arms may not be all that scary to 'Mechs or tanks, but when you encounter two-dozen guys who might as well be wearing Canopian swim trunks, you can do some serious damage in a way most 'Mech weapons can't. The way Dad tells it, you ain't never heard squealing until that jock in a *Hunchback* realizes he's about to get swarmed by guys with grappling hooks, satchel charges, and no pretty girl to go home to. Then it's all "Come save me, Leo! Don't let them get me, Leo!"

"Leo"—yeah, they named me after my grandpa. That story really happened, you know. He scrapes the groundpounders off the *Hunchback*—and takes a PPC to the face for his trouble. Apparently they had to use a vacuum cleaner to get what was left of him out of what was left of his cockpit to send home. But that guy in the *Hunchback*? He had "Duke" or "Count" or something in front of his name, so in some kind of publicity stunt they "gift" the 'Mech that got Grandpa killed to his family.

So naturally, it goes to my dad. And sure enough, he also signs up for the FWLM. Yeah, it turns out that brains ain't all that common in the Simonides family. I mean, sure, they were begging him, and Duke Hunchback paid his whole way through officer candidate school and everything. Set up Grandma and Aunt Thea for life, too.

Turns out Dad was a decent pilot. Emphasis on "was." No, he's still alive, not like Grandpa. But he was with the First Marik Militia on Megrez back in '18, and apparently things got so ugly he decided to hang up his cooling vest and move the whole family away from the front. Mom says he still wakes up screaming some nights.

That makes it my turn. Problem was, Duke Hunchback longer wanted to fund our family line for one lousy *Locust*, and if I'm being honest, I never had the discipline to join any proper military group anyway. Back when we lived on the Lyran border, Dad brought me by the base once or twice, and the place was just, I don't know, *wrong*. It was all cold and clean and antiseptic. Very professional, but not very homey, if you know what I mean. Definitely not for me.

So that left piracy and mercenary work, and it's kinda hard to get into the piracy gig when you live on Tamarind. Also, eye patches, peg legs, and parrot crap on my shoulder wasn't really a look I was into. I supposed I could've gotten a real job, but again, all of my forays into "legitimate work" left me kinda cold.

Which brings me to Galatea City and that noteputer with all the questions. I fill it out, and then…I wait. I mean, sure, there's a lot of units hiring, but there's also a lot of people looking for work. Far too many of them have much sexier rides than I do.

The mercenary hall is nice, but that's not where you get to wait for people to call you. So I found myself waiting in the same places where most business is actually handled—the various Mechjock bars that litter the area within a few blocks of the hiring hall. They're all right, I suppose. The beer is kinda cheap and the peanuts are free. There are even relatively few fistfights—even though most of the folks there are anxiously waiting for comm calls about potential employment, and are wound up tighter than myomer in a lightning storm.

When I finally do get a call, it's from a fellow named Stephen Lucius. He meets me in a bar called Marauder Bill's. It's got one of those LED lights that's supposed to look like ancient neon, but the *B* looks different from the rest of the letters, like it's been replaced recently. I get there first, find a nice little booth in the back, and order a Timbiqui Dark—what the heck, I'm about to get hired, right? Time to splurge. It's what all the cool mercenaries drink, after all.

I've only got a few minutes to enjoy my (admittedly decent) beer when Lucius walks in. He's in his fifties, maybe, with short brown hair and a bit of a scraggly brown beard with gray spots. He walks with a pronounced limp, and wears a sweat-stained jumpsuit that was probably House military once, but had the insignias carefully removed. Based on the discolored spots where the national insignia used to sit, I can't quite place which military it is, but I'm pretty sure it's not one of the big ones. He introduces himself, sits down opposite me, and orders some fancy Glengarry whisky I've never heard of.

"So here's the deal," he starts. He's got some weird accent I can't quite place. Periphery, definitely. Taurian, maybe? "I'm putting together a new kind of mercenary unit. Kind of a co-op. I'm looking for pilots who own their 'Mechs. We'll take work like usual, except that instead of getting a salary, you'll get a cut of the take. That's after repair, maintenance, ammo, and overhead costs are taken out. I'll provide the techs and other logistics, so all you need to do is show up and shoot who I say you should shoot."

Okay, I'm kinda embarrassed to admit that I'm not exactly sure how that differs from other mercenary pilot deals, so I don't say anything.

"Salvage rights will depend on various factors, of course, but the basic idea is every pilot on a mission will get paid a share of the market value of any salvage. When we salvage something that strikes your fancy, you can buy it off the unit. We'll even take your old ride as a trade-in. I'll be honest, I've got money, but not enough to hire really *good* pilots with really *good* 'Mechs, so our first few missions will likely be recon and stuff like that."

He's got a noteputer with a bunch of pretty graphs about pay expectations, maintenance costs, that sort of thing. His idea of a co-op mercenary unit is interesting, and I like the idea of them handling all the repairs and stuff. I know a little bit about how a 'Mech works, but not nearly enough to join one of these fly-by-night operations where the pilots do their own grease-monkeying. I've also certainly heard horror stories of pilots who failed to put the shielding back in place on their reactors properly before firing them up. Oh, sure, there's no *boom* or anything, but things like "radiation burns" and "carcinoma" aren't ones I feel like experiencing firsthand.

I tell him I'm interested, but naturally I gotta listen to all my other offers. No, I don't actually *have* any other offers yet, but he doesn't need to know that, does he?

"Understood," he says. "Get back to me when you decide. I'll be here for at least another week." He hands me his comm code on one of them old-fashioned business cards. He politely excuses himself, saying something about meeting other potential pilots, and leaves the bar.

I immediately wonder if he's as full of it as I am.

Still, he was polite and professional. That's pretty cool.

A few days later, I meet a guy recruiting for Wolf's Dragoons. No, not one of the guys you see on the cover of *Mercenary Monthly* (or the redhead—what's her name? Nancy? Natalia? Something like that). No, this was some kind of junior recruiting flunky. He might've just been some guy who picked up a uniform and insignia from a gift shop and was using it to scam wannabe MechWarriors out of free beer. Either way, I don't think he was all that impressed—he never called me back.

Next guy I meet is a kid named Carlyle, putting together a new unit. I mean, I know I'm young, but I swear he's like twelve. He's got the same questions as the last two, but then he hits me up with this one:

"Why do you want to be a mercenary?"

Shit. I got nothing. Seriously, I'd never really thought about it before. I mean, it just kinda seems obvious, doesn't it? Third-generation 'Mech pilot with his own ride and not a lot of life skills, what else am I going to do? I know better than to say "I hated all the other options," so I make up some BS about tradition and living up to my dad and grandfather's expectations. Problem is, he and I both know it's crap.

He gives me a polite goodbye and leaves with something akin to "Don't call me, I'll call you."

Eh. No big loss. I doubt he'll go far.

Over the rest of the week, I meet a couple of other recruiters. Some seem on the up-and-up, some seem super sketchy. Some want me to buy in to their units—if I had cash for that I wouldn't be here, would I?—and some are offering basically slave-labor wages or terms like "You pay us for repairs and consumables." I can't imagine anyone falling for that, but they seem legitimately surprised when I turn 'em down. So in the end, I call the first guy back.

"Steve! It's Leonidas Simonides." I try to sound all cool. I definitely don't want him to think that if I don't go with him I'll have to call back one of the guys who wants to sell me the same bullets he wants me to shoot at someone. "I'm in."

"Great, kid. I'll draw up a contract and send it over this afternoon. Have your lawyer look over it. If he has any questions, he can reach me here."

Heh. My lawyer. That's *rich*.

"Oh, and kid? That's the last time you ever call me 'Steve.' Got it?"

Gulp.

"Got it."

I actually do try to read all the fine print on the contract. I'm not a lawyer, but it all looks okay, so I sign on the dotted line. Why not? It's not like I'm rolling in better offers.

Lucius runs a more impressive operation than I'd originally thought. When I show up at the spaceport, I find he's got a pair of *Union*-class DropShips. They look like they're in pretty decent shape. They've got similar paint schemes to Colonel Lucius' uniform—like he's trying to hide an old affiliation or something. Of course, half the *Union*s in the Inner Sphere have changed hands so many times in the last 300 years that if you scraped off the paint, you'd find layers of half a dozen different nationalities on them, so that's nothing new.

He's got a group of maybe two-dozen other pilots with their 'Mechs lined up on the tarmac when I get there. It's kind of a neat group, really, from all over the Inner Sphere. Sure, the guys with spurs on their boots are giving a wide berth to the guys with swords in their belts, but they're all here together. Apparently, love of money is more important to your average merc—even wannabe mercs like these guys—than loyalty to a nation.

The 'Mechs themselves are a rather ragtag bunch. Most of them strike me as family heirlooms like my own, and none are bigger than a *Panther*. I really hope I don't find myself in a fight against anything big—one competently driven heavy 'Mech could probably take us all out before we even got in range. There's quite a variety, though, everything from classics like *Locust*s and *Stinger*s to some random stuff I barely recognize. Is that a *Firefly*? Didn't those all go extinct in the First Succession War?

Lucius steps forward, distracting me from my impromptu game of "Name That 'Mech."

"Okay, boys, listen up. Welcome to the Lancers. I've secured us a contract where we can start to earn our rep. Sure, it's a bug hunt at the far end of the FedSuns, but it's a good way to cut our teeth, and maybe even upgrade some of our hardware before we go up against anything really dangerous."

Okay, first of all, "boys"? That's a little condescending, isn't it? Heck we're not all even *male*...

Second, what the hell's a "bug hunt"?

According to the murmurs going around the crowd, we're apparently going after pirates. Something about them scattering like cockroaches or something. Whatever. It's not sexy, but Lucius is right—it's a good way to get started. He says some more stuff about logistics and everybody getting along despite coming from different backgrounds and how "you're all in this together." Finally, he dismisses us to meet with our company commanders.

Mine is a relatively young woman named Mel Archer. She's from Shoreham, on the FedSuns-Cappie border. Apparently she's some kind of war hero, although if that's true, why'd she leave the FedSuns' military? Her ride's a *Valkyrie*, and unlike my "brand-new" *Locust*, I'm pretty sure that thing saw General Kerensky himself jump off into the sunset.

Mel's nice enough, if a bit squirrely, like she's worried people are gonna figure out she's not all that. She tells me I'll meet the rest of my company over the next couple of days while we burn for the jump point, but I should start by meeting up with Scotty, our chief tech.

Oddly enough, Scotty's real name is James O'Malley. I find him in one of the *Union*'s cavernous cargo bays, supervising the loading and securing of our 'Mechs. He's holding a cup of coffee in one hand and a noteputer in the other, and he's shouting orders to astechs when I walk up. I try to give him my best salute, but he just grunts at me and tips his head a notch.

"Simonides," he says after I give him my name. "The LCT-1V, right?"

I nod.

"Nice 'Mech. No serious complaints. The Martell needed tuning, of course, and there was some balding in the myomer insulation on the thigh of the right leg, but otherwise a fine ride that's clearly been professionally maintained. Hell, you even have maintenance logs going back until the thing walked out of the factory. That's a nice change. I'm pretty sure several of these 'Mechs have had their logs blanked to cover for the fact that they're stolen. I try to tell most folks I meet in this line of work that I really don't care where their 'Mechs come from, but I *do* care if there's a jury-rigged polarity swap on the PPC feeds that's gonna fry the first astech who takes them apart without fully flushing the capacitors first."

I smile and nod some more. Like I said, I know some basics, but for the most part, I have no idea what he's talking about. I'm pretty sure "the Martell" is the laser. I remember seeing one of their ads, "Victory at the speed of light" or something. Still, it turns out he likes my 'Mech, so that's a thing. He promises to take good care of "her" and then gets back to work.

Did you know 'Mechs were female? Yeah, me neither.

Scotty seems legitimately disappointed that my 'Mech doesn't have a name. I'll be honest, the thought never occurred to me. As far as I know, neither Dad nor Grandpa ever felt obligated to name it, so why should I? Maybe in a few generations, when it's as old as some of the other 'Mechs I've seen, someone will give it a name, but for now, it's "it."

After that I get to meet my new bunkmates. Due to the limited space on *Union*s, there's three of us in the cabin. Besides me, there's Pat, a *Mongoose* pilot who's actually from Terra, and Sam, the guy with that *Firefly* I saw earlier. Pat and I are both in Company A, Recon Lance. Sam's not with us, though, because his 'Mech is too slow. Different lance, same company. We've barely had five minutes to get to know each other when the ship's sirens start blaring to let us know it's time to prep for takeoff.

I don't know if you've ever been in a *Union* that's taking off, but it's pretty exciting. I mean, this ship is older than dirt, and yet for centuries it's been throwing superheated plasma out its nethers fast enough to make a building fly. It rattles and shakes the whole time, and you're getting pushed into your seat at a minimum of twice the force of Terra's gravity. I think maybe Pat hasn't been involved in too many takeoffs, because even with the beers Sam smuggled out of the commissary for us, he's clearly a bit nervous.

But here's the thing—when Pat gets nervous, he starts talking. And he's *hysterical.* He starts telling us this story about how he got his 'Mech. He claims he stole it from a museum in Geneva. I don't believe a word of it, but I don't really care, either. At one point, just as I'm taking a swig from my bulb of beer, he describes the cockpit of his "newly purloined 'Mech" as "smelling like a century of butt-sweat." I laugh so hard beer comes out my nose.

By the time he's done telling his story, we've broken atmo and are making a leisurely half-g burn toward the jump point, where a JumpShip will be waiting to carry us to our destination.

You know, it's funny. I really didn't know what I was getting into when I left Tamarind to come to Galatea. I had some ideas about what I *didn't* want to do, but I wasn't really sure if the mercenary life was the one for me. Heck, I guess I won't really know that until after I've had a battle or two under my belt. Still, after less than a day with these folks, I already feel something—a sense of belonging maybe—that until now I never even knew was what I was looking for.

Damn it. Now I know what I should have told that Carlyle kid.

BATTLETECH ERAS

The *BattleTech* universe is a living, vibrant entity that grows each year as more sourcebooks and fiction are published. A dynamic universe, its setting and characters evolve over time within a highly detailed continuity framework, bringing everything to life in a way a static game universe cannot match.

To help quickly and easily convey the timeline of the universe—and to allow a player to easily "plug in" a given novel or sourcebook—we've divided *BattleTech* into eight major eras.

STAR LEAGUE
(Present–2780)
Ian Cameron, ruler of the Terran Hegemony, concludes decades of tireless effort with the creation of the Star League, a political and military alliance between all Great Houses and the Hegemony. Star League armed forces immediately launch the Reunification War, forcing the Periphery realms to join. For the next two centuries, humanity experiences a golden age across the thousand light-years of human-occupied space known as the Inner Sphere. It also sees the creation of the most powerful military in human history.

(This era also covers the centuries before the founding of the Star League in 2571, most notably the Age of War.)

SUCCESSION WARS
(2781–3049)
Every last member of First Lord Richard Cameron's family is killed during a coup launched by Stefan Amaris. Following the thirteen-year war to unseat him, the rulers of each of the five Great Houses disband the Star League. General Aleksandr Kerensky departs with eighty percent of the Star League Defense Force beyond known space and the Inner Sphere collapses into centuries of warfare known as the Succession Wars that will eventually result in a massive loss of technology across most worlds.

CLAN INVASION
(3050–3061)
A mysterious invading force strikes the coreward region of the Inner Sphere. The invaders, called the Clans, are descendants of Kerensky's SLDF troops, forged into a society dedicated to becoming the greatest fighting force in history. With vastly superior technology and warriors, the Clans conquer world after world. Eventually this outside threat will forge a new Star League, something hundreds of years of warfare failed to accomplish. In addition, the Clans will act as a catalyst for a technological renaissance.

CIVIL WAR
(3062–3067)
The Clan threat is eventually lessened with the complete destruction of a Clan. With that massive external threat apparently

neutralized, internal conflicts explode around the Inner Sphere. House Liao conquers its former Commonality, the St. Ives Compact; a rebellion of military units belonging to House Kurita sparks a war with their powerful border enemy, Clan Ghost Bear; the fabulously powerful Federated Commonwealth of House Steiner and House Davion collapses into five long years of bitter civil war.

JIHAD
(3067–3080)

Following the Federated Commonwealth Civil War, the leaders of the Great Houses meet and disband the new Star League, declaring it a sham. The pseudo-religious Word of Blake—a splinter group of ComStar, the protectors and controllers of interstellar communication—launch the Jihad: an interstellar war that pits every faction against each other and even against themselves, as weapons of mass destruction are used for the first time in centuries while new and frightening technologies are also unleashed.

DARK AGE
(3081-3150)

Under the guidance of Devlin Stone, the Republic of the Sphere is born at the heart of the Inner Sphere following the Jihad. One of the more extensive periods of peace begins to break out as the 32nd century dawns. The factions, to one degree or another, embrace disarmament, and the massive armies of the Succession Wars begin to fade. However, in 3132 eighty percent of interstellar communications collapses, throwing the universe into chaos. Wars erupt almost immediately, and the factions begin rebuilding their armies.

ILCLAN
(3151-present)

The once-invulnerable Republic of the Sphere lies in ruins, torn apart by the Great Houses and the Clans as they wage war against each other on a scale not seen in nearly a century. Mercenaries flourish once more, selling their might to the highest bidder. As Fortress Republic collapses, the Clans race toward Terra to claim their long-denied birthright and create a supreme authority that will fulfill the dream of Aleksandr Kerensky and rule the Inner Sphere by any means necessary: The ilClan.

CLAN HOMEWORLDS
(2786-present)

In 2784, General Aleksandr Kerensky launched Operation Exodus, and led most of the Star League Defense Force out of the Inner Sphere in a search for a new world, far away from the strife of the Great Houses. After more than two years and thousands of light years, they arrived at the Pentagon Worlds. Over the next two-and-a-half centuries, internal dissent and civil war led to the creation of a brutal new society—the Clans. And in 3049, they returned to the Inner Sphere with one goal—the complete conquest of the Great Houses.

SUBMISSION GUIDELINES

Shrapnel is the market for official short fiction set in the *BattleTech* universe.

WHAT WE WANT

We are looking for stories of **3,000–5,000 words** that are character-oriented, meaning the characters, rather than the technology, provide the main focus of the action. Stories can be set in any established *BattleTech* era, and although we prefer stories where BattleMechs are featured, this is by no means a mandatory element.

WHAT WE DON'T WANT

The following items are generally grounds for immediate disqualification:

- Stories not set in the *BattleTech* universe. There are other markets for these stories.

- Stories centering solely on romance, supernatural, fantasy, or horror elements. If your story isn't primarily military sci-fi, then it's probably not for us.

- Stories containing gratuitous sex, gore, or profanity. Keep it PG-13, and you should be fine.

- Stories under 3,000 words or over 5,000 words. We don't publish flash fiction, and although we do publish works longer than 5,000 words, these are reserved for established *BattleTech* authors.

- Vanity stories, which include personal units, author-as-character inserts, or tabletop game sessions retold in narrative form.

- Publicly available *BattleTech* fan-fiction. If your story has been posted in a forum or other public venue, then we will not accept it.

MANUSCRIPT FORMAT

- .rtf, .doc, .docx formats ONLY
- 12-point Times New Roman, Cambria, or Palatino fonts ONLY
- 1" (2.54 cm) margins all around
- Double-spaced lines
- DO NOT put an extra space between each paragraph
- Filename: "Submission Title by Jane Q. Writer"

PAYMENT & RIGHTS

We pay $0.06 per word after publication. By submitting to *Shrapnel*, you acknowledge that your work is set in an owned universe and that you retain no rights to any of the characters, settings, or "ideas" detailed in your story. We purchase **all rights** to every published story; those rights are automatically transferred to The Topps Company, Inc.

SUBMISSIONS PORTAL

To send us a submission, visit our submissions portal here:
https://pulsepublishingsubmissions.moksha.io/publication/shrapnel-the-battletech-magazine-fiction

The march of technology across BattleTech's eras is relentless...

RECOGNITION GUIDE: ILCLAN VOL. 01

RECOGNITION GUIDE: ILCLAN VOL. 02

RECOGNITION GUIDE: ILCLAN VOL. 03

RECOGNITION GUIDE: ILCLAN VOL. 04

RECOGNITION GUIDE: ILCLAN VOL. 05

RECOGNITION GUIDE: ILCLAN VOL. 06

Some BattleMech designs never die. Each installment of *Recognition Guide: IlClan*, currently a PDF-only series, not only includes a brand new BattleMech or OmniMech, but also details Classic 'Mech designs from both the Inner Sphere and the Clans, now fully rebuilt with Dark Age technology (3085 and beyond).

STORE.CATALYSTGAMELABS.COM

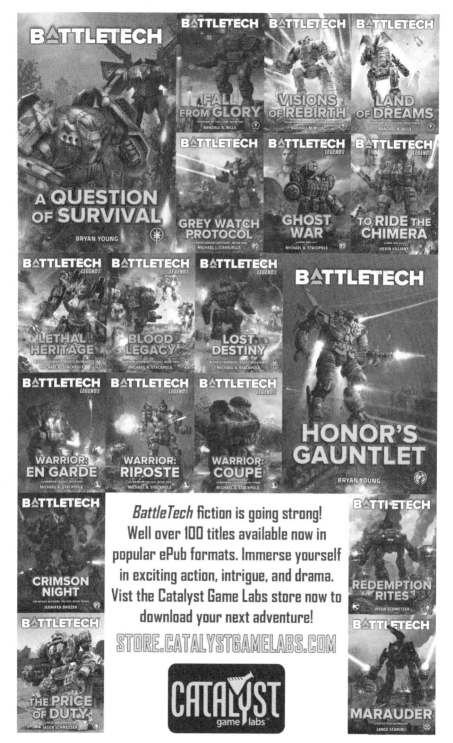

Made in the USA
Las Vegas, NV
10 December 2024

13804732R00134